D0903480

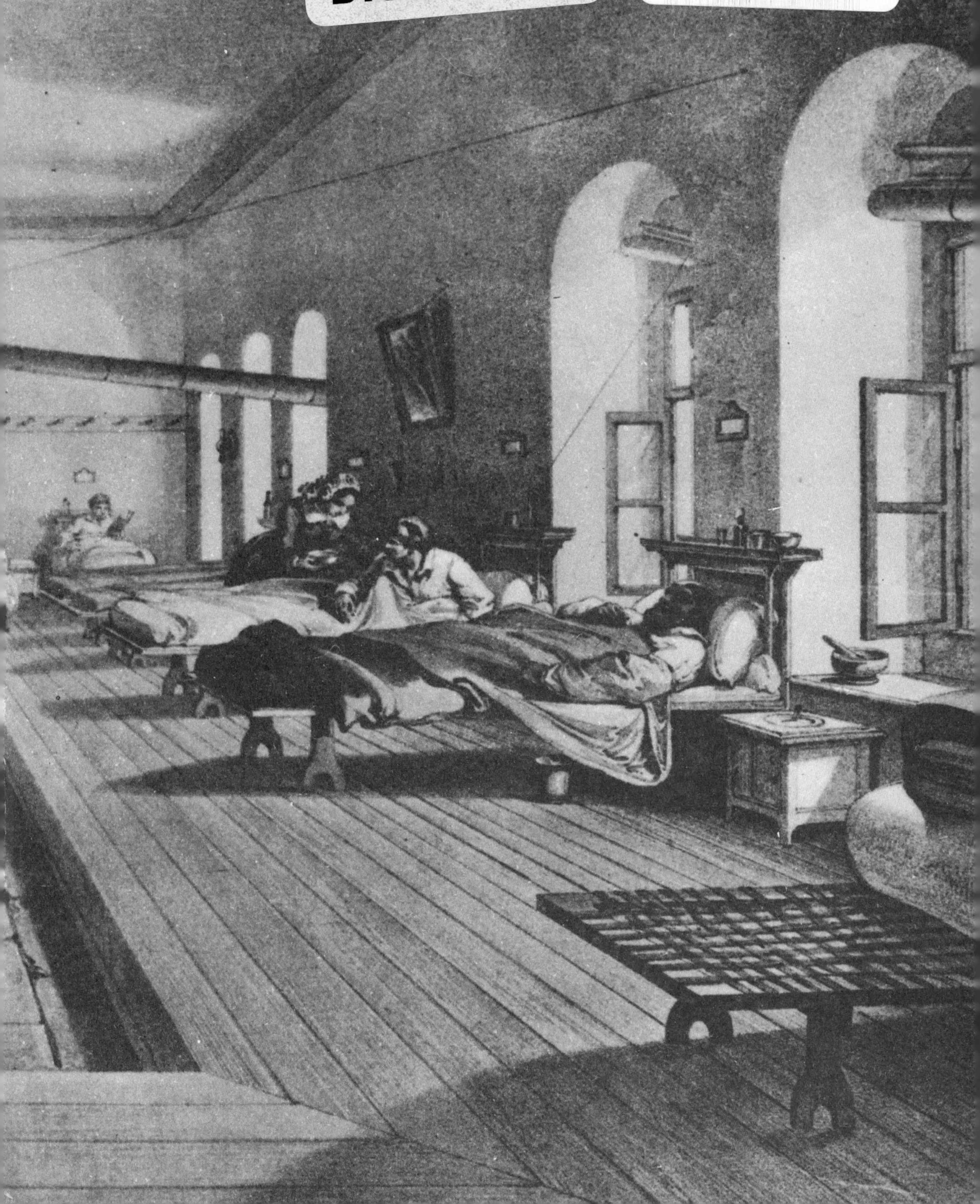

G

The Wonderful World of Medicine

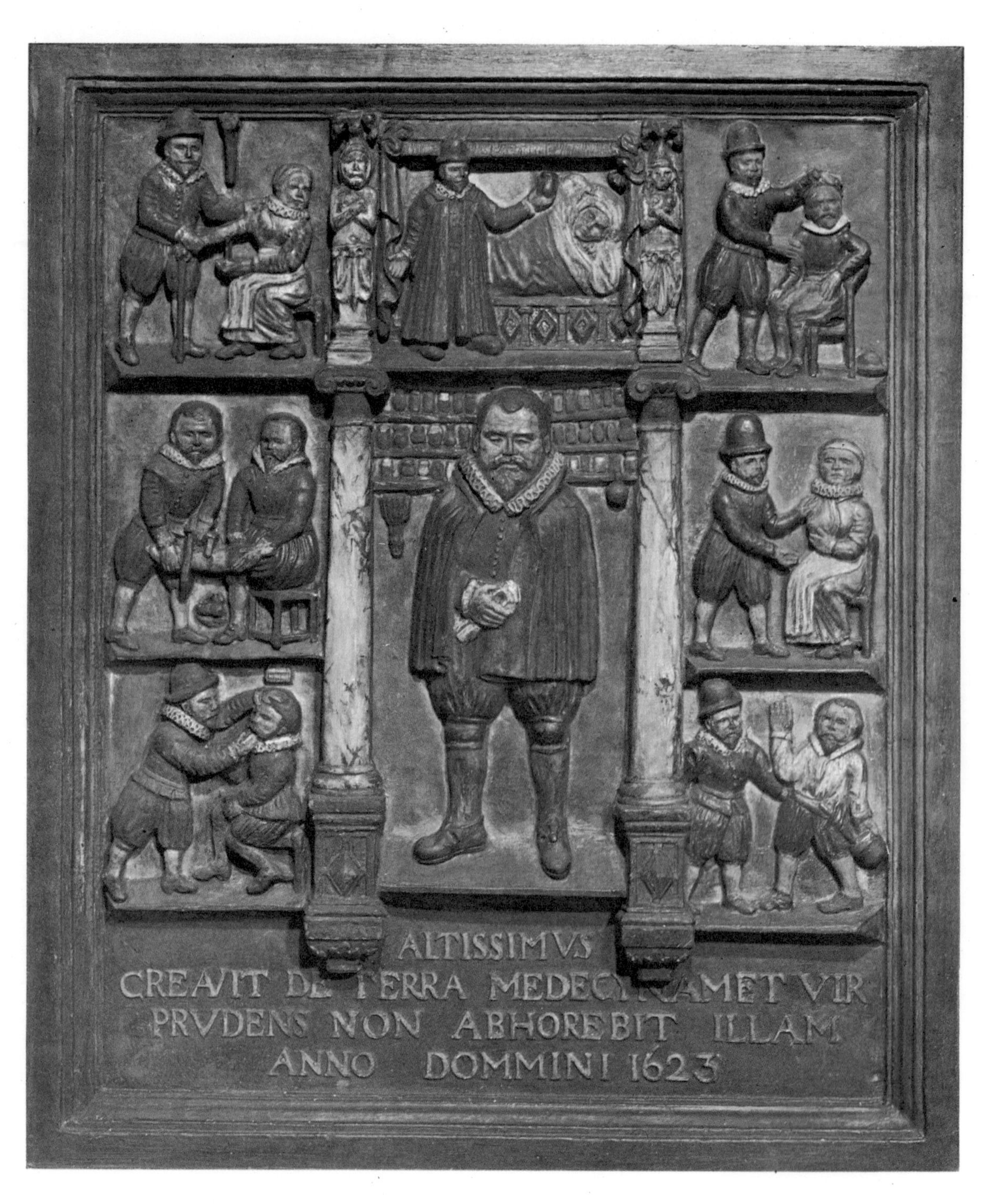

The painted wooden signboard of a surgeon-physician of 17th-century England.

The Wonderful World of Medicine

Ritchie Calder

Doubleday and Company Inc.

Garden City, New York

Library of Congress Catalog Card Number 68-14989

Printed in Yugoslavia

Contents

Certain words and phrases in this book are followed by the symbol☞. Whenever you see this symbol it means that you can look up the word or phrase in the alphabetical glossary at the end of the book and find more information or a fuller definition of the term.

1 The Miracle of Man

Magic is primitive man's first response to the illnesses that beset him. Faced with a disaster for which he has no natural explanation, he seeks a supernatural cause. Everywhere medical lore grew up around the belief that the world swarmed with spirits that afflicted living creatures with disease, just as they fired forests with lightning, stopped the rains, or sent the floods. To make these spirits more real, primitive man set up idols to represent them and worshiped them with ritual offerings. As belief in an afterlife developed, there came a new fear—fear of the unhappy spirits of the dead who would, if neglected, return to plague the living. Then, too, there might be danger from human enemies who worked by spells and sorcery and had to be fought with their own weapons.

Complicated rites and counter-spells needed experts: and the witch doctor became a powerful figure in primitive society. He dressed grotesquely to impress not only the spirits but also his patients. His costume was part of his bedside manner.

He had to practice not only white magic but black as well. The first was "good medicine," even if the witch doctors used fearsome-sounding spells to coax the spirit of sickness out of the patient. The second was "bad medicine," or the working of evil.

But the craft of the witch doctor was not all magic. He knew how to suck poison out of wounds and how to apply poultices. He might ascribe mystical properties to herbs and administer them with elaborate ceremonies, but he learned which should be prescribed when, and he handed on his knowledge to those who came after him.

With the coming of the first city civilizations in Egypt and Mesopotamia, rituals grew still more complicated and the priesthoods came into being. The early temples were colleges where priests collected and recorded facts. They noted how changes in the positions of certain constellations regularly coincided with events like the ripening of crops,

African nail fetish and mask, supposed to protect the owner against disease.

the flooding of rivers, the outbreak of disease. Gradually they came to believe that the stars exerted an influence on man and that different parts of the body, like different plants, were under the influence of the 12 signs of the Zodiac. A trace of this belief still lingers in the word "lunacy"—mental sickness supposed to be due to the moon. It is interesting that early Chinese doctors, who inserted needles into "channels of the body" to "let in fresh spirits," used 365 different needling-points, the same number as the days in the year.

Even now, despite the vast array of laboratory drugs and the battery of electronic instruments at his command, the modern physician still owes something to folklore, "wise women," alchemists, and priest-physicians. Quinine, prepared from the bark of a tree, was originally the ritual medicine of the Incas of Peru, and is still valid as a cure for malaria; penicillin comes from a mold, providing scientific justification for the age-old custom of applying molds to septic sores.

The present-day practitioner even owes a debt to the witch doctor's "showmanship," which impressed the treatment on the patient. The modern physician may know how diseases are caused and how drugs work within the living body. He may diagnose with accuracy and prescribe with certainty: but his profession still calls for something more. So it must be. Sick in mind or body, the patient of today needs reassurance as much as primitive man.

Many thousands of years were to pass before our ancestors were able to break free from superstition and to understand the natural causes of disease. In the interval, however, they were gradually building up a picture of those most complicated of all creatures—themselves. Like any student learning anatomy today, they started with the skeleton. Bones are the only permanent records of prehistoric medicine. From recently discovered bones of early men we can tell that some of them suffered from such diseases as rickets and arthritis☞.

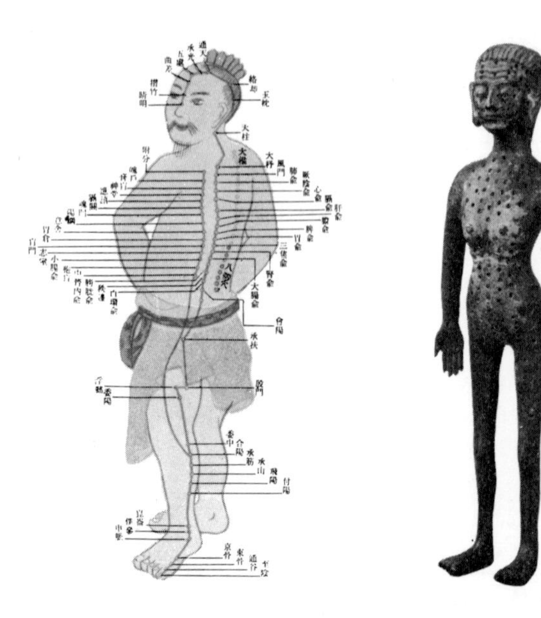

Left, traditional Chinese diagram and model of a man, showing some of the 365 needling points that are still used in acupuncture.

Opposite, a 16th-century physician uses a pulley to reset a dislocated arm.

These early ancestors must often have seen skeletons and recognized the difference between human ones and those of the animals they hunted. They seem to have been especially interested in the skull, perhaps because—unlike the rest of the framework—it could *hold* something: indeed, they themselves could use it as a cup or casket. Large numbers of prehistoric skulls have been dug up in different parts of the world, many with holes in them—holes deliberately made with sharp flint instruments. In many cases, new bone has grown around the hole, proving that this first of all surgical operations (trephining) was performed on a living patient who survived. In some skulls, more than one hole has been found, suggesting that a series of attempts had been made to release "spirits" from the casket, perhaps to relieve an attack of madness, an epileptic fit, or simply a severe local headache.

From dead bones early man discovered his own framework: the casket of the skull; the basket-work of the ribs; the vertebral bones of the spine; the pillars of the limbs. He found that certain joints fit into sockets and perhaps realized that a dislocated joint can be put back into place. By painful experience he probably learned that a broken bone would mend if rested for a time. Bone-setting was one of the earliest forms of surgery.

Though the geography of the dead skeleton had been charted by the Middle Ages, the skeleton within the living body did not become visible until the end of the 19th century. In 1895 a German professor of physics, Wilhelm Röntgen of Würzburg, was experimenting with a vacuum tube. He was passing an electric current through it when he found that, although the tube was completely enclosed in a cardboard container, a fluorescent screen nine feet away was glowing. Invisible rays were passing right through the cardboard. He found that when he put his hand in front of the tube, the shadow of his bones was visible on the screen. When he moved his fingers he could see the skeleton at work.

The medical men of his time were quick to realize the value of these *X rays*☞, as Röntgen named them. Within a year or two of his great discovery, X-ray apparatus was installed in many hospitals as an aid to the bone-surgeon. Since that time doctors have also learned how certain of the internal organs can be photographed by means of X-ray apparatus.

When, fresh from his course in 20th-century medical science, the newly fledged doctor examines his first patient and writes ℞ at the top of his first prescription, he is invoking (though he may not know it) a god of ancient Egypt. 𓂀 was the symbol for the eye of Horus, the hawk-headed sun-god who lost his eye in battle and had it restored by Thoth, the god of wisdom. Horus was one of the many deities invoked by the doctors of ancient Egypt when administering their remedies.

Despite their mystical methods, these priest-physicians knew the value of several practical remedies, including senna and castor oil. Egypt's great contribution to medicine, however, came not from the doctors but from the embalmers who worked in the House of the Dead. Writings of the period show that, through embalming, the Egyptians of 5000 years ago had a greater knowledge of the organs than those who came after them—Greek, Roman, and medieval physicians.

In preparing mummies they had to remove the organs before steeping the body in resins and spices, and wrapping it in strips of fine linen a thousand yards long. Many of our modern methods of bandaging are derived from those used in the swathing of these ancient mummies.

Doctors of later civilizations were, in general, discouraged from dissecting the human body. Not until the 16th century of our own era did the Christian Church begin to relax its anti-dissection regulations. About a century later, with the help of the newly invented microscope, the Italian anatomist Marcello Malpighi was able to start a detailed study of the liver, kidneys, and spleen. But even today their functions are not fully explained.

In the middle of the 18th century, Leopold Auenbrugger of Austria invented percussion, a method doctors use to diagnose conditions

Left, Imhotep, the ancient Egyptian doctor who became god of medicine.

Opposite, the structure of the lungs shown in a photograph of lung tissue injected with plastic.

of the lungs. As a boy he had frequently watched his father tap barrels to see how much wine they contained. Now he tapped the chests of his patients. If they gave out the hollow sound of empty barrels, they were healthy; a muffled or high-pitched note indicated the presence of unhealthy fluid.

Memory of an everyday scene played a part, too, in the invention of the stethoscope. In 1816 the French physician René Laënnec was called to the bedside of a woman suffering from heart disease. She was rather stout and Laënnec decided that it would be of little use to apply his ear direct to her chest. Suddenly he remembered some children he had seen at play. One had been scratching the end of a log while his friend listened at the opposite end. Laënnec rolled up a piece of paper, put one end to his ear and the other to his patient's chest. He could hear the heart beating more clearly than ever before. Delighted, he experimented with other materials, finally deciding that wood was the most effective.

The first insight into the digestive system came through "St. Martin's Window." In 1822 Alexis St. Martin, a Canadian fur-trapper, was wounded in the stomach during a brawl near Lake Michigan. He recovered, but the wound left a permanent hole through which Dr. William Beaumont of the United States Army was able to watch how the stomach exudes the juices needed for digestion.

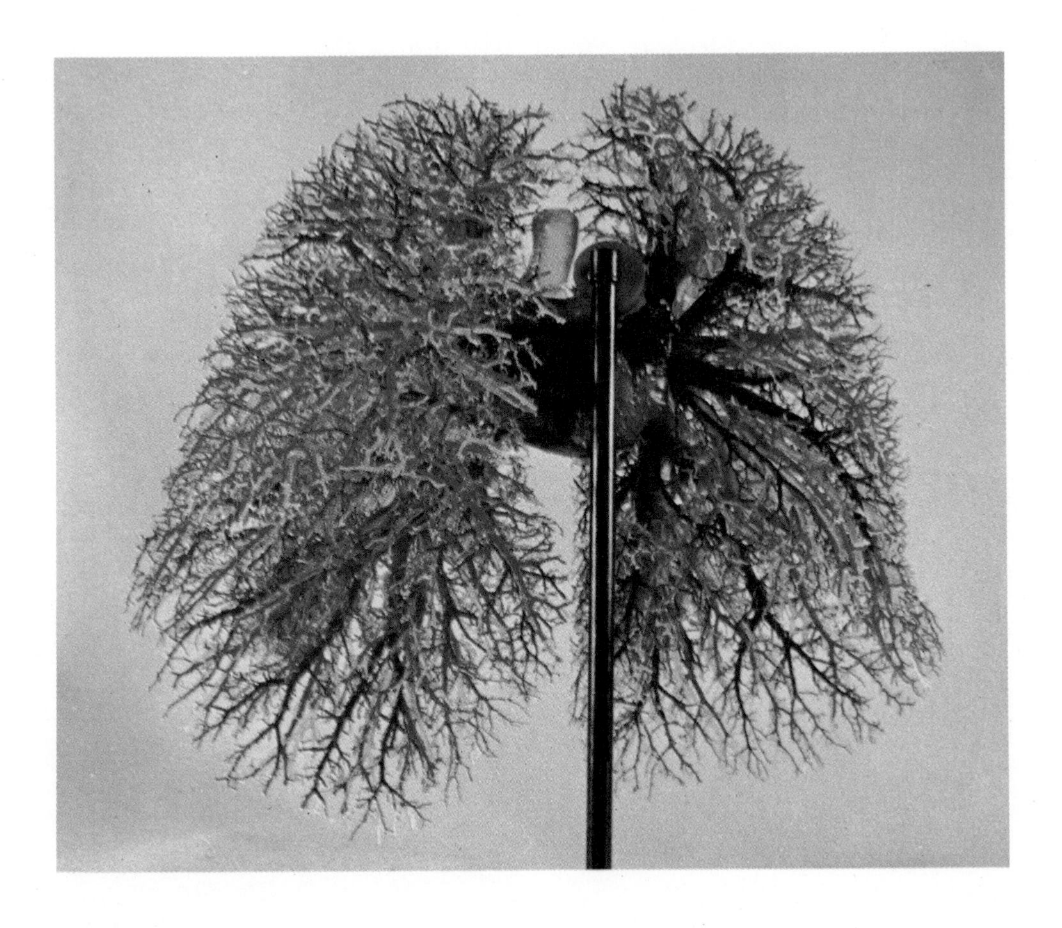

The Greeks may have been behind the Egyptians in knowledge of the organs, but they had little to learn from them about the muscles. The artists of ancient Greece studied as thoroughly as the physicians how the muscles manipulate the skeleton. Their "life class" was the athletics field, where naked youths wrestled, jumped, ran, or threw the discus. Greek sculptors such as Praxiteles and Lysippus (fourth century B.C.) could carve details of muscle-structure that even a conscientious medical student of the 20th century might overlook.

The great artists of the Renaissance—Michelangelo, Raphael, Dürer, Leonardo da Vinci—also produced works of art perfect in anatomical detail. Not satisfied with superficial observation, some turned anatomist. Leonardo dissected over thirty bodies, and made hundreds of sketches.

One of the great years in the history of medicine was 1543, when Andreas Vesalius of Brussels published the first comprehensive textbook of human anatomy, *De Humani Corporis Fabrica* [On the Fabric of the Human Body]. The text was as remarkable as the illustrations, which have been attributed to students of the great artist Titian. Vesalius was a rebel against the medical teachers of his time, who relied chiefly on classical literature. According to them, Aristotle, the Greek philosopher of the fourth century B.C., and Galen, who lived some four hundred years later, had discovered all there was to know about the human body, though in fact their writings were based mainly on the dissection of animals. Vesalius insisted that the proper book to study was the body itself. To get "subjects," he would steal out of Paris at night and cut down the bodies of robbers from the gibbets of Montfauçon. At the age of 23 Vesalius became professor of anatomy at Padua, the leading

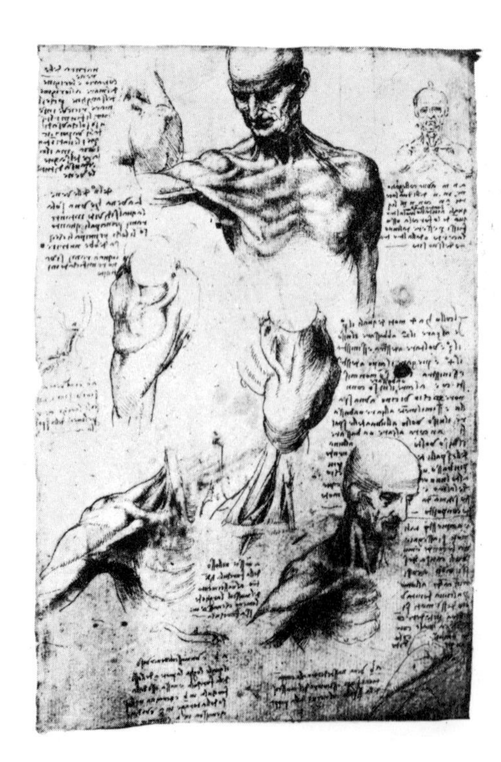

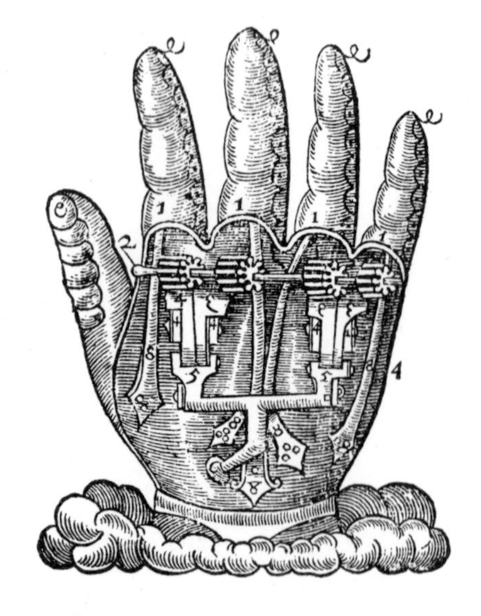

Left, anatomical drawings by Leonardo da Vinci (1452-1519). Above, engraving of an artificial hand designed by Ambroise Paré (1517-90).

medical school of his day. Students from all over Europe crowded the tiers of the arena where he lectured. By admitting nothing except what he himself had seen, he turned anatomy into a science.

A contemporary of Vesalius and a great admirer of his work was Ambroise Paré, a barber-surgeon in the French army. He spent most of his life on the battlefield, where he took the then revolutionary step of washing wounds with spring water, applying soothing ointments and clean bandages, tying arteries☞ to staunch the flow of blood. Paré studied the action of the muscles: how they always pull and never push the limbs; how the muscles on the front of the arm pull to bend the elbow and the muscles on the back pull to straighten it. He used his knowledge to make mechanical limbs for crippled soldiers. The artificial arm that he designed, based on the mailed gauntlets of the knights of chivalry, was the forerunner of many of the ingenious devices that today enable limbless people to lead active lives.

It was not until the 19th century that scientists discovered that the muscle machinery of the body needs sugars as fuel. The process by which muscles respond to electrical impulses that travel to them along the nerves remained a mystery until the 20th century. Then research showed that the nerves not only carry the signals for movement but also release a substance that makes the muscle contract and other substances that counteract it, wiping out the tension.

In this field, as in others, medicine still makes use of primitive discoveries. In 1584 the great explorer and adventurer Sir Walter Raleigh introduced curare into Europe. Curare is a poison with which, for centuries, South American Indians have tipped their blowpipe darts. It paralyzes the prey, killing when it reaches the muscles used in breathing. Today the surgeon employs a small amount of a substance derived from curare in conjunction with an anesthetic☞ to stop the twitching of muscles during an operation.

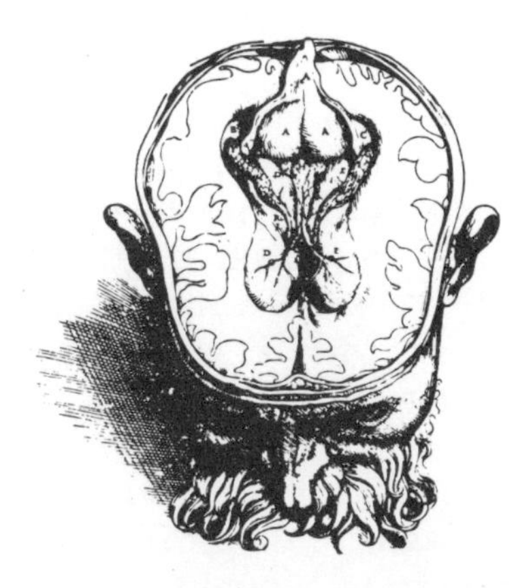

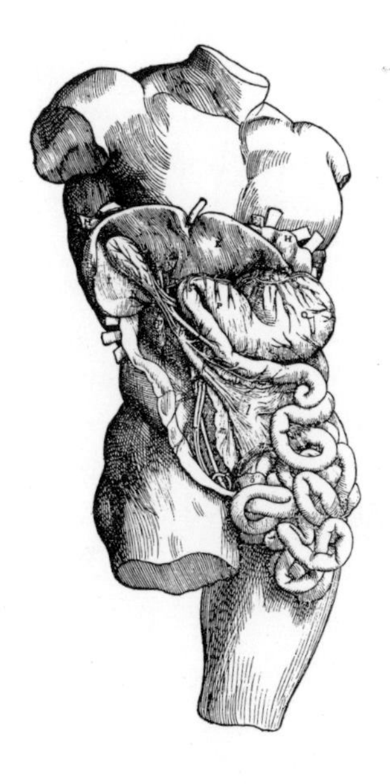

Above and right, two illustrations from De Humani Corporis Fabrica, *the great anatomical textbook by Andreas Vesalius (1514-64).*

The Chinese *Canon of Medicine*, said to have been written about 2600 B.C., declares: "All the blood of the body is under the control of the heart and flows in a circle and never stops." That was 4000 years before Dr. William Harvey explained the process.

Harvey was born at Folkestone, England, in the year 1578. At the age of 20 he went to Padua to study under the famous anatomist Fabricius, who had discovered what he called "the doors of the veins"—the valves that turn the veins into "one-way streets" so that the blood in them must always travel toward the heart.

Harvey, in his experiments, found that the great arteries carry the blood *away from* the heart. He noticed two other things: that a bulkhead in the heart prevents the blood passing from one side to the other; and that the left part of the organ pumps out some two ounces of blood each time it beats. He reasoned that this blood must go somewhere to make room for more. He showed that the left side of the heart forces blood into the arteries, which carry it through the body; the blood returns through the veins, and the right chamber of the heart then pumps it through the lungs. From there it returns, purified, to the left chamber, ready for redistribution. On its journey, as we now know, it carries oxygen to the tissues of the body, including the muscles, and the chemicals from digested food needed to nourish and repair the cell structures of the body. When disease invades the body, it is the blood that carries the garrison (antibodies☞) to repel the attack and the white cells (or leucocytes☞) to surround the invading germs. The blood also helps to heal wounds; it contains a substance that causes it to clot in air and so seal the opening while the skin-tissue forms again.

Blood-letting is one of the oldest forms of medical treatment: the bleeding-glass formed part of the symbol of the physician in ancient Egypt, and for centuries the blood-sucking leech was regarded as an essential part of the doctor's equipment in Western Europe. Harvey's discovery now led to the first attempts at blood-giving. Among the early experimenters was Sir Christopher Wren, architect of St. Paul's Cathedral in London. In 1665, eight years after Harvey's death, Richard Lower successfully transfused blood from one dog to another through a quill. Attempts to transfuse the blood of animals into men, however, were usually fatal; often, too, the linking of the blood vessels of two humans caused death. The cells of the blood might clump together or those of the patient might break up. The reason became obvious only at the beginning of this century, when it was found that people belong to different blood groups that may conflict with each other when mixed.

Although transfusion was tried in the First World War and during the Spanish Civil War, its use did not become widespread until the Second World War, when many thousands of air-raid and battle

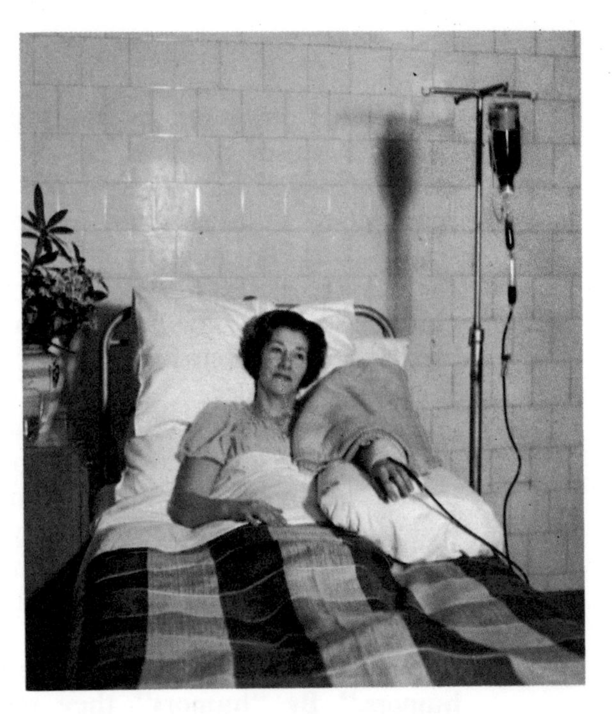

Above: left, an 18th-century doctor makes a fatal experiment—transfusing blood from a lamb to a man; right, in a modern hospital, transfusion saves lives.

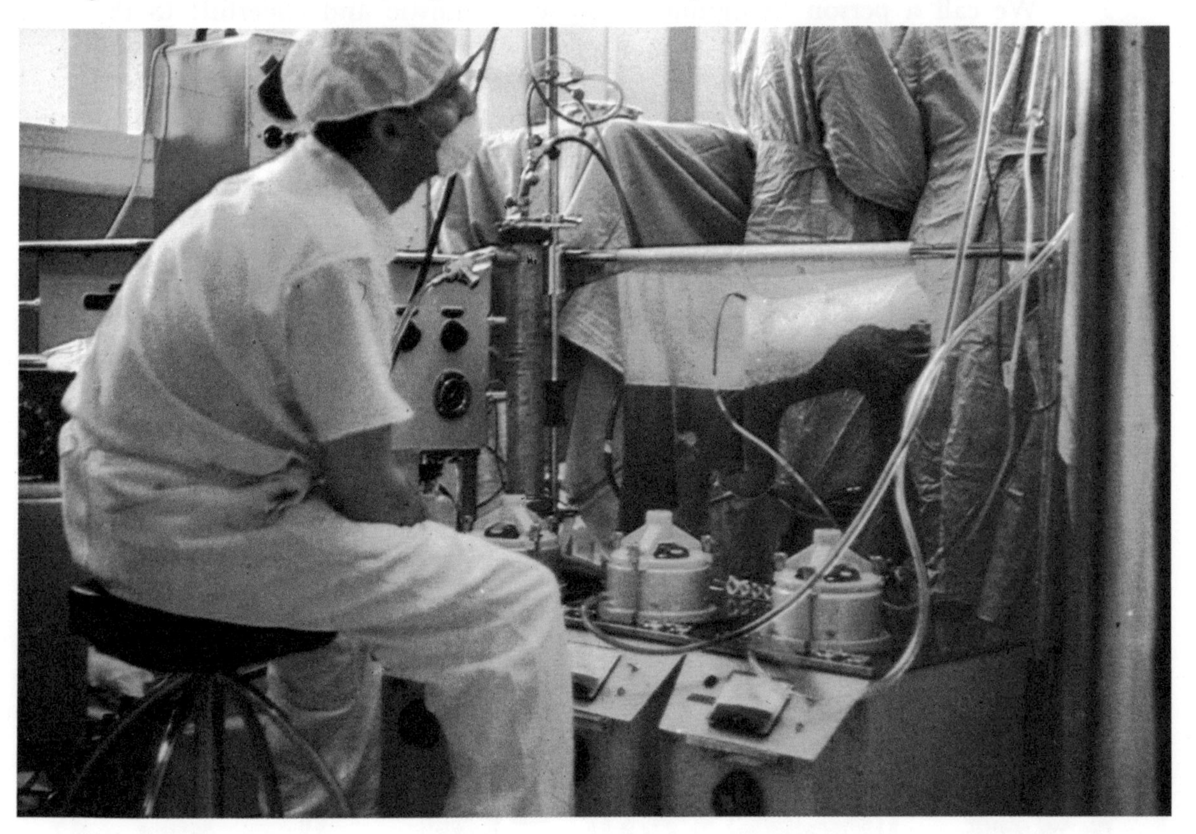

Today surgeons use the heart-lung machine to keep the blood circulating through a patient's body while his heart is out of action during an operation.

You touch a hot cinder, your finger recoils, and you utter a cry of pain. In a split second, an impulse has traveled from the nerve-endings in the skin to the local control station in the spine; from there a second impulse has gone out to other nerves, which have instantly contracted the muscles, withdrawing the finger and preventing further hurt. Simultaneously the brain has telegraphed a message to the vocal chords and lips: you say, "Ouch!"

This illustrates something of the immense complexity of the central nervous system☞ and the diversity of impressions that pour into it.

The brain receives these impressions from nerve-endings all over the body, and proceeds to sort them out. On the tongue there are "taste buds." Some of these are connected to brain cells that register sweet things, while others connect with "sour," "salt," or "bitter" areas. In the same way light waves received by the eye, and sound vibrations picked up by the ear, are transformed into electrical impulses that pass to the appropriate brain cells. The brain also stores up impressions in the "area of memory"—the filing-cabinet from which we produce the picture of a past scene, the scent of a childhood garden, or just the fact that two and two make four. It is also concerned with passing judgment.

Many of our actions are *voluntary*—based on decisions of the conscious mind, as when a driver swerves to avoid another car. But many others, such as withdrawing the finger from a hot cinder are *involuntary*—controlled by nerve-centers outside the brain. Others are *conditioned*, such

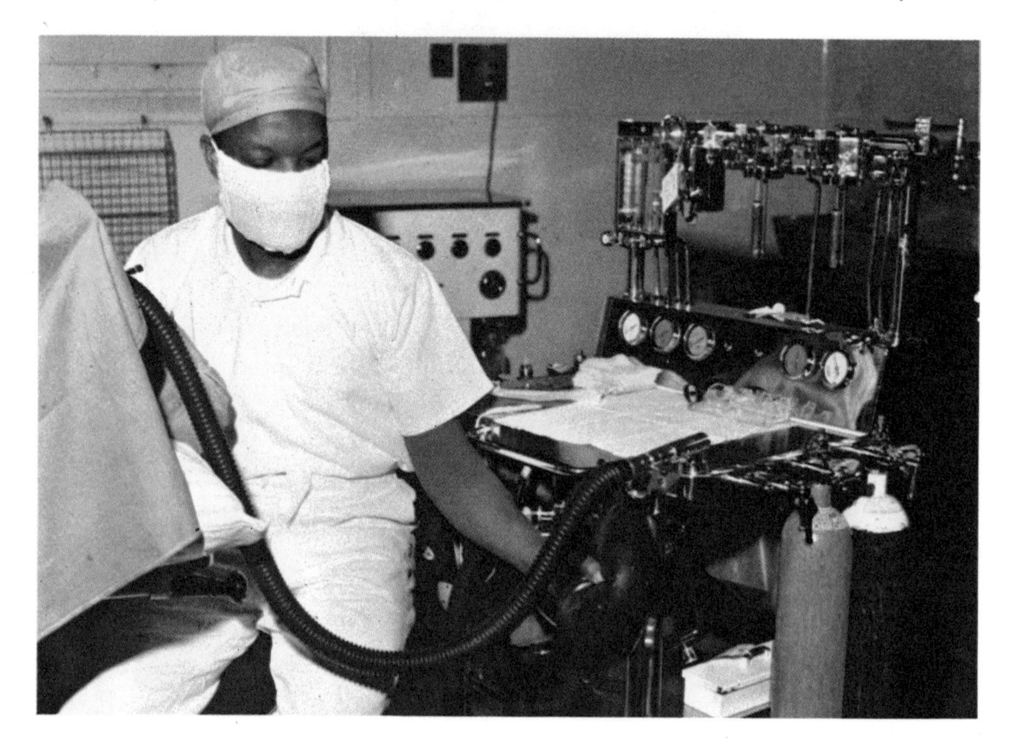

as the mouth watering because a smell suggests a dish once enjoyed. Digestion and blood-distribution depend on the self-regulating, or *autonomic*☞, nervous system.

During the 18th century, Luigi Galvani showed that the leg muscles of a dead frog contract as a result of electrical stimulation of the nerves; but not until this century could doctors explain the electrical basis of the nervous system.

Today, with a machine called an *electroencephalograph*, we can record the electrical impulses of the brain cells in much the same way as we record the impulses of the heart with the electrocardiograph☞. The nervous system, however, is not only electrical; it is also chemical. As we have seen, the chemicals it releases make the muscles contract; but chemicals can also act on the nerves—a discovery that led to control of pain by anesthetics. Among the pioneers of general anesthesia were three Americans. Crawford Long of Georgia used ether for a painless operation in 1842. In 1844, in Hartford, Connecticut, a dentist named Horace Wells used nitrous oxide (laughing gas) to make himself unconscious while a colleague extracted a molar. In 1846 William Morton used ether to anesthetize a patient in a Massachusetts hospital, and John Warren performed a minor operation. In 1847 J. Y. Simpson of Edinburgh, Scotland, discovered the value of chloroform by trying it out at a dinner party. Today local and spinal anesthetics can render part of the body insensitive without producing unconsciousness.

Opposite, modern anesthetics cause loss of sensation, making surgery painless. Below, James Simpson's dinner-party experiment with chloroform (1847). Right, when we sip nasty medicine, "taste buds" send impulses to brain cells, and we wince.

The terms "mind" and "brain" are always liable to be confused, since physical damage to the brain can produce some types of mental illness, and surgical operations can sometimes cure them. Yet many diseases of the mind occur when there has been no apparent physical damage to the brain, and there are many forms of mental treatment other than surgery.

The witch doctors and priest-physicians, who knew nothing of the working of the physical *brain*, knew a great deal about treating the *mind*. The spells and incantations with which they administered their remedies were a form of mental treatment, as was the way they persuaded their patients that the demons of disease were being driven out.

To our forefathers, the mentally sick, with their delusions and wild actions, seemed like people in the power of devils. They chained them and beat them in an effort to destroy or drive out the evil spirits. In the 18th century, horror at such ill-treatment made Philippe Pinel of France, Benjamin Rush of America, and William Tuke of England campaign to unchain the mentally ill and to abolish the cages in which they were exhibited like animals. These were first steps toward the view that there is nothing supernatural about mental illness, which we should accept with common sense, just as we accept physical sickness.

The greatest advance, however, came with the work of Sigmund Freud. In 1885, soon after he had qualified as a doctor in his native Vienna, Freud went to the famous Paris hospital of La Salpêtrière. There he was greatly impressed by Charcot's experiments in hypnotism☞. Freud came to the conclusion that there are mental processes that go on behind the human consciousness, and "secret" memories that may influence and perplex conduct. Putting a patient into a trance helps to remove his conscious resistance to disclosing truths that have become buried; but, as Freud found, hypnotism is not essential, provided the patient is sufficiently relaxed. Once he becomes aware of the hidden truths that are causing his condition, his symptoms often disappear.

Freud and two of his students, Carl Jung and Alfred Adler, gave a new insight into the way the mind works. Today we know that not only unconscious memories, but also heredity (the characteristics passed on from generation to generation) and environment (the social and material conditions in which we live), have a certain part to play in influencing our state of mind.

Ivan Petrovich Pavlov, a contemporary of Freud, showed that conduct is also bound up with the nervous system. His most famous experiment was to ring a bell before giving meat to a dog: after he had done this repeatedly, the dog's mouth would begin to water merely at the sound of the bell. Such a reaction is called a "conditioned reflex." A dog can be "conditioned" to distinguish between two musical notes by receiving meat with one but not with the other. If the difference between the notes is too small, the nervous system does not know when to release the saliva; the dog becomes excited and develops a disorder of the nervous system.

These experiments illustrate the interplay between mind and body, and how it influences daily life. Today many people, especially those in highly responsible positions, develop stomach ulcers☞, heart trouble, or diseases of the blood vessels. The stress and worries of modern living may produce physical illness and, conversely, physical illness may produce mental anxieties. The word used to describe this interplay is *psychosomatic*☞—from "psyche," meaning mind, and "soma," body. This word forcibly reminds us that the Whole Man is not just a skeleton, with muscles, organs, nerves, brain, and mind, but a complex entity in which all these parts interact to produce a human personality.

Like all other living things, human beings not only exist, they also reproduce; and it is extraordinary that mankind took so long to reach any real understanding of the process.

It is true that some 2300 years ago Aristotle had studied the development of the chick within the egg, yet not until the 17th century of our era was it recognized, or at least recorded, how the cell within the hen

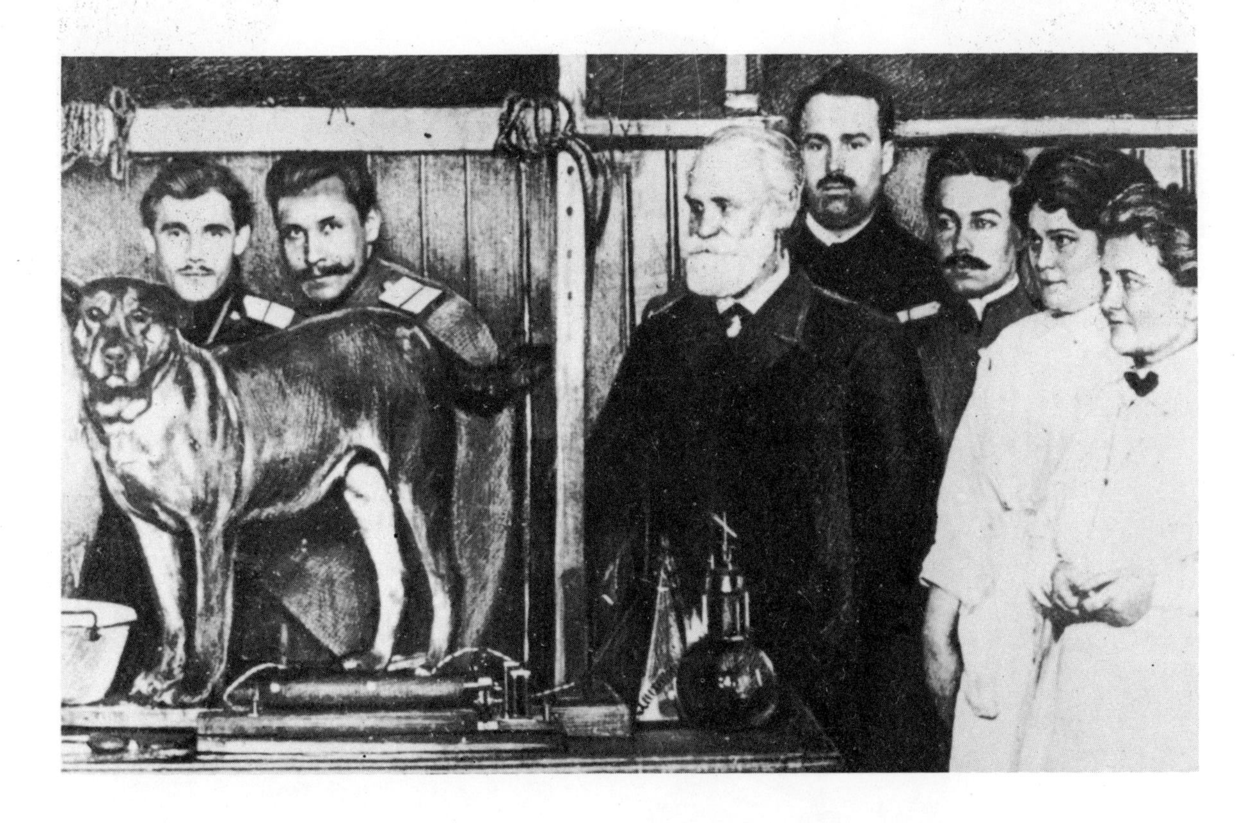

Russian physiologist Ivan Pavlov (1849-1936), photographed with his research team and the dog he used in his famous experiment on conditioned reflexes.

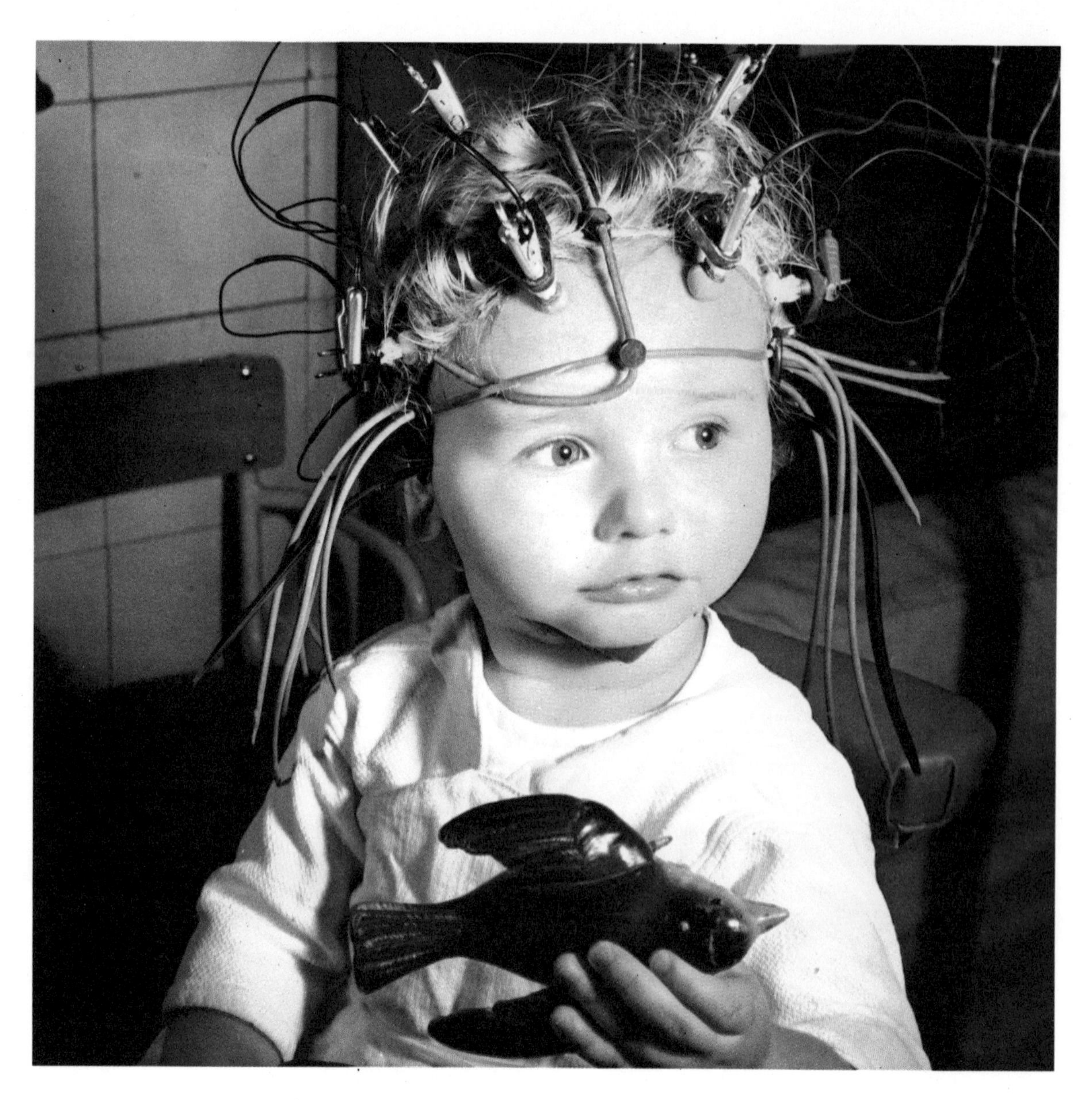

Above, the electroencephalograph can detect and record electrical impulses as they are emitted by the brain.

Left, a 17th-century doctor pictured man's mind as a universe, with its own "worlds" of senses, intellect, and imagination.

When the nucleus of a fertilized cell divides, each chromosome also divides. Finally the whole cell splits into two, each one identical with the other.

became an egg to be laid. This is the more remarkable when we consider that throughout that time poultry was being plucked and cleaned daily for cooking. Two hundred years later Karl Ernst von Baer of Estonia discovered the ovum, or egg-cell, in the female mammal.

Not until 1875, when Oskar Hertwig made the discovery, was it known that in fertilization the male sperm enters the female ovum; only then does a new creature take shape inside the female body.

Just before Hertwig's discovery, an abbot named Gregor Mendel had begun a close study of the peas he grew in his garden in Czechoslovakia. From this quiet hobby was to come the whole complex science

People with one red-haired parent are seldom red-haired, though they may carry a "red" gene. If two such people marry, red hair may appear in their children.

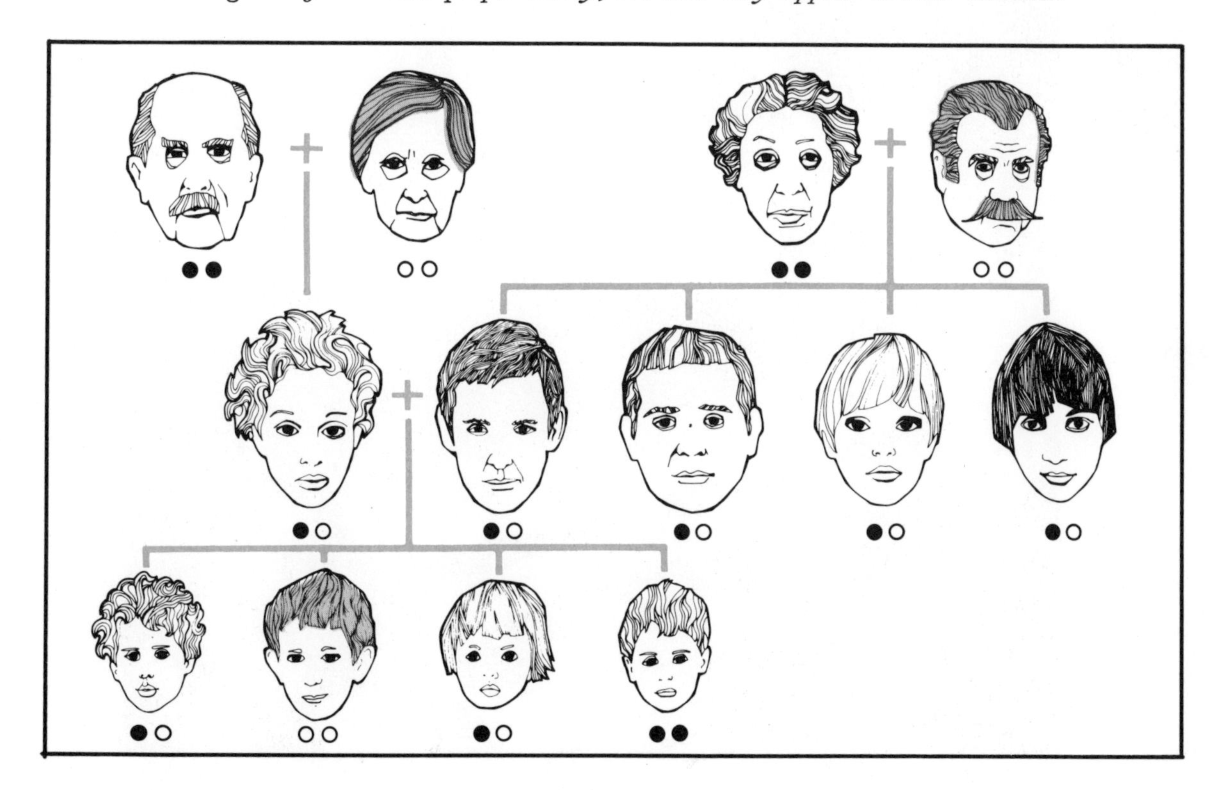

of genetics, which explains family resemblances. Previously people had thought that a child possessed a blend of the traits of his parents as a result of the mingling of blood. "It's in his blood," they would say. According to this idea, a father with curly hair and a mother with straight hair would probably produce a child with wavy hair—something between curly and straight. Mendel showed that inherited qualities are passed on not in the blood, but in the *genes*☞. The word *gene*, like *genesis*, is derived from the Greek for creation, or beginning.

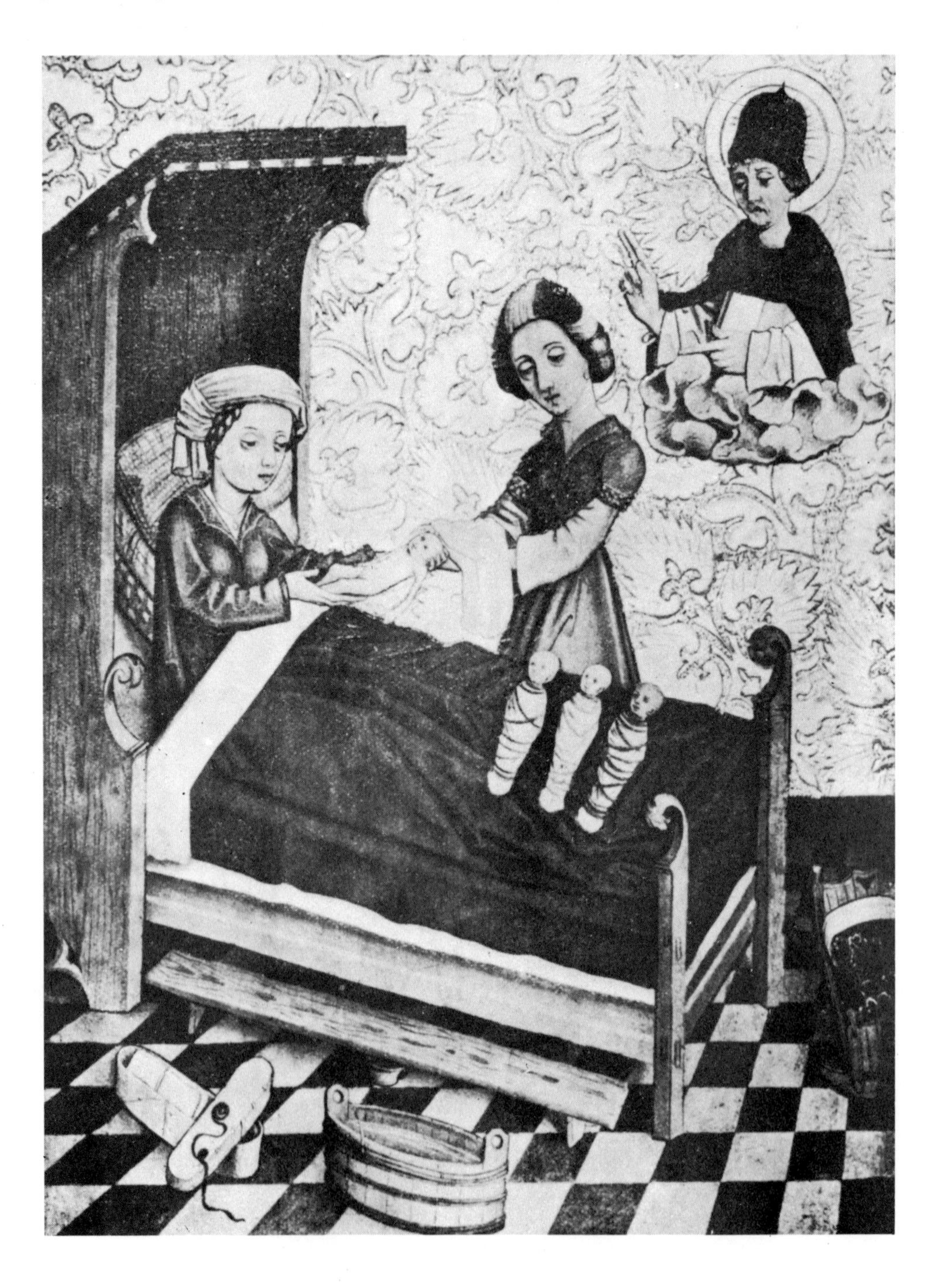

Genes are the atoms of life and, though larger than the atoms of matter, can scarcely be seen individually, even through the most powerful microscope. However, packages of them—called *chromosomes*☞—are visible under the microscope. Every human cell contains 48 of these chromosomes—with the exception of the male sperm and the female ovum, which have 24 each.

This ensures that when union occurs between sperm and ovum the sum of the new cells so formed will have "fair shares" of father's and mother's genes.

Though it may seem strange to compare a human child with Gregor Mendel's peas, in fact the same laws of heredity apply. Mendel crossed a strain of tall pea plants with a dwarf variety. All the first generation were tall because the gene that made the tall plants tall was "dominant"—that is, stronger than the one that made the short peas short. By crossbreeding among this generation he produced a new batch in which the short plants reappeared, one to every three of their tall brother peas. What happened was that the "short" genes had been there all the time and, in this second generation, the plants had received a "short" gene from both parents. The combination had produced more short plants.

Since the beginning of this century intensive research has gone on into the whole question of heredity, and genetic scientists can now calculate what parental characteristics are likely to appear in children.

Man's picture of himself has not taken shape in isolation. It has influenced, and been influenced by, technical achievements in other fields. Since the action of a piston-shaft turning a wheel has much in common with that of a human arm turning a mangle, it is only natural

Opposite, a 15th-century painting that shows a saint appearing at the birth of quadruplets.

Right, Gregor Mendel (1822-84), the Silesian botanist who discovered the laws of heredity.

A robot programmed to imitate human limb movements takes over household tasks: pushing the baby and cleaning the car.

that the scientists of the 19th century, the Age of Steam, should have thought of the body as a kind of steam engine. To them food was fuel and the stomach a furnace to be stoked.

Today we have come to realize that the body is less like a simple machine than like a complex group of factories under one central direction. We can compare the digestive system to an extremely complicated oil refinery. Food itself is not only energy-fuel, but also the raw material from which the laboratories of the glands extract rare chemicals. The blood vessels are pipelines that transport these chemicals—as well as gases and liquids—to the various body tissues; they also carry off waste products.

Engineers continue to learn from medical scientists, who in turn are helped by the engineers. Limb movements have been magnified in giant mechanical cranes. Heating engineers have learned much about air-conditioning from the body's thermostatic control of its own temperature. The snorkel submarine imitates the respiratory system. The television camera has mimicked the way in which the human eye and nervous system convert visual images into electrical signals. The microphone is like the human ear, changing sound vibrations into electric pulses. The loudspeaker, like the vocal chords, changes electric pulses into sounds, and the tape recorder "memorizes" these sounds. Electronic instruments, ranging from those that control a whole factory to those that can pick up the most delicate objects without damage, duplicate human touch. Indeed the only senses we have not successfully imitated are those of taste and smell; and there are as yet no machines possessing the human powers of imagination, will, and judgment.

Every advance in the technical field brings home yet again how wonderful the human body is. For example, the human brain weighs about three pounds and fits into the casket of the skull, with a capacity of 85 cubic inches. It contains perhaps 10,000,000,000 cells, each equivalent to a radio valve. The body-generated electricity it uses is about enough for a bedside reading lamp. If engineers were to reproduce that brain, using the tiniest of modern valves in place of the cells, they would need a concert hall to house it and the electricity supply of a city to provide its power.

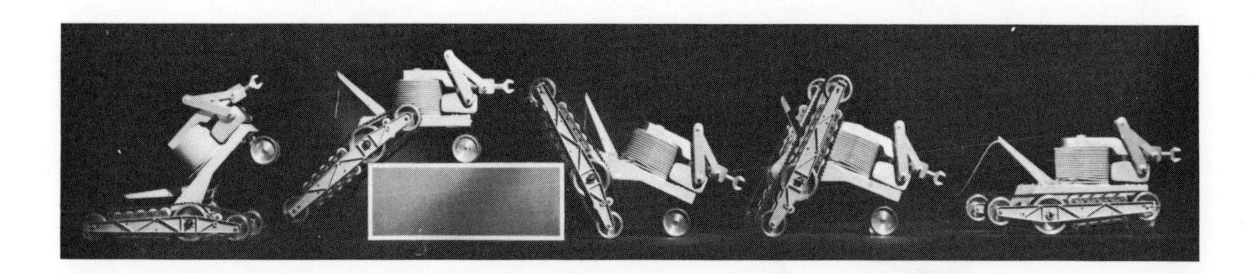

Working model of a remote-controlled inspection vehicle and handling device, designed to operate in radioactive environments that would be fatal to man.

2 The Devils of Disease

A shoal of fish, a flock of birds, a herd of animals—the words remind us that living creatures seldom exist in isolation. Man is no exception. He is a member first of the family, and the family in turn is part of a wider community.

One of the smallest of such groups is the primitive hunting community. The medical problems of such a group are not very complicated. In the first place, by a process we call "natural selection," the individual suffering from a hereditary weakness seldom survives. If an Eskimo hunter has poor eyesight, he will lose his way. If he is born a cripple, he will not be able to keep up with the group. Either way he will probably die young.

Then, too, the size of the group and its isolation ensure that its members are less exposed to infectious diseases than people in crowded towns. But, should an infectious disease be introduced from outside, it will often be fatal, since members of the group will have no "natural immunity." Eskimos have died as the result of colds that would be considered no more than a sniffle in communities where colds are common. In the Arctic, as in hot, arid deserts, airborne germs do not survive easily, and the chief dangers to health are from animals. Eskimos may contract disease from the Arctic hare or take in parasites☞ with the fish and meat they eat raw.

By age-old experience such hunting groups have learned what food they need and what to avoid—such as polar bear's liver, which is so rich in vitamin ☞A as to be poisonous. Eskimos living on their traditional foodstuffs have fine eyesight, healthy teeth, strong bodies, without any knowledge of diet sheets or vitamins. Their teeth do not decay; they get worn down, like those of an old dog. By experience, too, they have learned how to treat wounds, broken bones or teeth, and damaged eyes.

Faced with conditions such as delirium, which they cannot rationally

An American Indian witch doctor with his "magic" drum (engraving of 1841).

explain, they turn to the witch doctor, or *shaman*. Though an ordinary member of the group, he may then assume a mask, go into a trance, and communicate with the spirits to the accompaniment of chants and the beating of drums. Since, as we have seen, mind and body interact, these weird rituals, designed to win the confidence of the patient, are often remarkably effective.

When scattered, wandering people began to congregate in settled communities and cities grew up, medical problems increased. Very early on, inhabitants of great towns seem to have realized how diseases spread when large numbers of people are crowded together. The Phoenicians, for example, worshiped Beelzebub, "Lord of the Flies." These insects, which can carry deadly diseases from person to person, were never allowed inside his temple. Though the people of Mesopotamia held that the stars and demons affected the human body, they also had some perfectly sound ideas about the cause and prevention of illness. Their systems of public drains and cesspits diminished the risk of infection from pollution. They knew, too, that leprosy was transmitted by contact between individuals and they expelled the leper from the community. "Never more shall he know the ways of his abiding place," says an inscription dating back more than 3500 years.

One stage in the development of Mesopotamian medicine was described by Herodotus, the great Greek historian who visited the city of Babylon in the fifth century B.C. He wrote: "They bring their sick into the marketplace. Then those who pass by the sick person confer with him about his disease and discover whether they have ever been afflicted with the same disease and advise him of the treatment by which they or others have been cured."

Some authorities have suggested that this procedure was used only by those who were too poor to afford the services of a doctor, for by the time of Herodotus, the Babylonians had already had a medical service for some two thousand years. In the case of internal complaints they turned to the priest-physicians, or *ashipu*, who made a diagnosis after direct examination of the patient or after studying a specimen of his

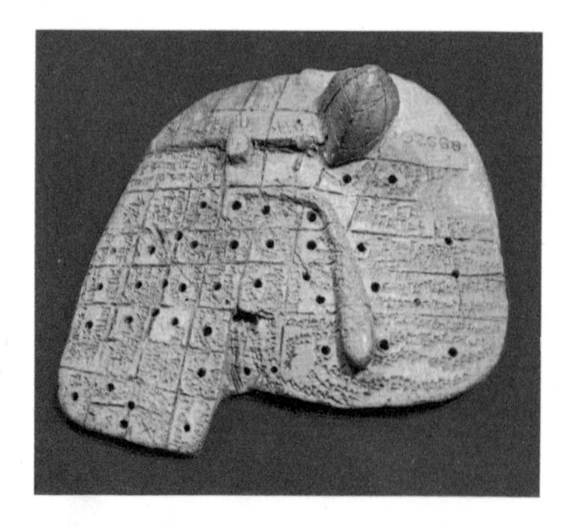

Left, ancient model of the sheep's liver consulted by Babylonian doctors forecasting the course of an illness.

Opposite, ancient Egyptian sculpture showing a priest with a limb atrophied by poliomyelitis.

blood. In the case of an important patient the physician would often sacrifice a sheep and inspect its liver in the belief that this would reveal to him the future course of the complaint.

From the lists of prescriptions and treatments written on clay tablets it is apparent that the ashipu, like their contemporaries in ancient Egypt, had shrewd knowledge of practical remedies, despite the fact that they frequently added revolting ingredients to otherwise useful drugs. These ingredients, like the ugly images set up at the doors of houses, were intended to drive away demons.

When afflicted with wounds, sores, or other external injuries Babylonians turned to the *asu*, or surgeons. While the priests were answerable to the gods, the asu were answerable to the state. The Code of the great king Hammurabi, dating from about 2000 B.C., sets out the regulations governing the practice of the asu and lists the fees payable. For example: "If the doctor shall treat any gentleman and shall open an abscess☞ with a bronze knife or shall preserve the eye of the patient, he shall receive ten shekels of silver. If a patient be a freeman he shall pay five shekels. If the patient be a slave the owner shall pay two shekels."

But woe betide the nonpriestly doctor if he failed. If he killed the patient or destroyed the eye, his hands were cut off—unless the patient were a slave: then the asu had to recompense the owner.

In ancient Greece magic merged into medicine, and mythology into clinical practice. Apollo, god of the elements whose arrows spread disease, had an earth-born son, Aesculapius, who studied medicine under Chiron the centaur. Aesculapius saved so many lives that Pluto, god of the Underworld, complained to Zeus that his kingdom was being diminished. Zeus obligingly slew Aesculapius with a thunderbolt, later transforming him into a god.

That is the legend. Quite probably Aesculapius was a real person whose medical reputation, like that of Imhotep in ancient Egypt, was so great that he came to be regarded as a god. His son Machaon was, according to the poet Homer, the hero-surgeon smuggled into besieged Troy inside the wooden horse. Three more of his children—Telesphorus, god of convalescence, Hygeia, goddess of public health, and Panacea, the herbalist, whose name we still apply to "cure-all" remedies—appear on the tablets presented to the Aesculapian temples of healing by patients who had been cured.

These temples were set up by the worshipers of Aesculapius in wooded groves; on admission the patient's confidence was won by showing him the tablets. Treatment, which included diets, massage, and mineral baths, was prescribed according to the patient's dreams. Priests came round followed by sacred snakes (the serpent is still the symbol of healing) that were supposed to lick the sore places of the patients.

Philosophers as well as priests studied medicine. One of the most famous was Pythagoras, who taught that number was the basis of all things; another was Empedocles, who taught that man was composed of the four elements: earth, air, fire, and water. These attempts to reduce the causes and cures of all diseases to a single, all-embracing system, though an oversimplification, were an advance on the superstition that attributed disease to the arrows of Apollo.

It was Hippocrates who put Greek medicine on a firm foundation by insisting that the physician's proper place was the bedside, and that every patient presented a separate problem. The casebook attributed to him contains records of actual patients with symptoms so carefully observed that modern doctors can diagnose the complaints. Today this great physician, born in the fifth century B.C., is still regarded as the supreme example of the "good doctor," and the oath that has governed the conduct of the medical profession for centuries is known as the Hippocratic Oath.

In the days of the Roman emperors, Greeks were accepted first as army doctors, then as family physicians. About A.D. 170, when Marcus Aurelius fell ill, he called in Galen, a Greek. So shrewd an observer was Galen, and so great a gatherer of medical information, that his word was law for over 1400 years, until Vesalius began to question it.

The greatest contributions of the Romans were in the fields of army surgery, for which they devised ingenious instruments, and of public health. Their aqueducts brought 250 million gallons of fresh water daily to Rome. Some, like the great Cloaca Maxima sewer, are still in use today.

A landmark in the history of medicine was the founding of Christendom's first medical school at Salerno, in southern Italy. The school, said to have had its beginning in the fourth century A.D., exercised its greatest influence from the 10th to the 12th century—the great age of the Crusades. According to tradition its founders were "Four Masters"—Pontus, a Greek; Adala, an Arab; Salernus, a Latin; and

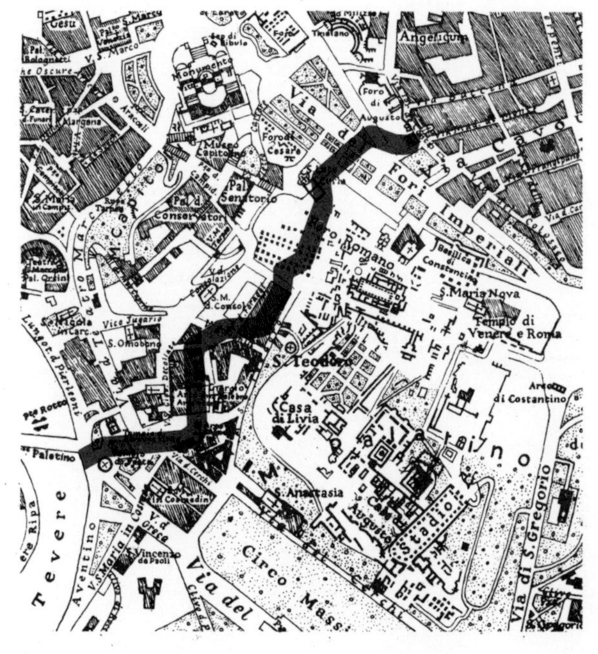

Left, an ancient Greek tablet depicts a physician examining a young patient. Right, red line marks Rome's ancient Cloaca Maxima sewer, still in use today.

Elinus, a Jew. The story of the Four Masters is perhaps no more than a parable to illustrate the four mainstreams of learning—Greek, Arabic, Roman, and Hebrew—that met at Salerno, where students of all races, women as well as men, worked together.

To these four mainstreams, older civilizations had contributed their own lore and experience, not only those of Egypt and Mesopotamia, but also of south and east Asia. Far to the east, Chinese medicine can trace its own system of rules back to about 2600 B.C. The *Canon of Medicine*, which had its origin at about that time, but which was doubtless amended in later centuries, contained not only an account of the circulation of the blood but also detailed instructions about such matters as taking the pulse. Chinese practices and remedies filtered into Persia, where the priest-physicians or *Magi* (from which we derive the word *magic*) used herbs to fight the disease-demons or *drogues* (from which we derive the word *drugs*). About A.D. 850, when the Muslim Empire reached the height of its glory, Arab doctors acquired Chinese knowledge—not only from the Persians, but also by direct contact with China itself.

India, too, made important contributions to the mainstreams. One of the great works of Indian medicine, the *Rig Veda*, dates from 1500 B.C., and by 300 B.C. hospitals were in existence. The Indians were expert at eye and plastic surgery, and adept in the setting of fractures with splints. By the fifth century A.D. Indian doctors had learned that mosquitoes carry malaria and rats the plague.

Muslim medicine not only absorbed knowledge, but also added new drugs to the pharmacist's list and produced many remarkable physicians. In the ninth and tenth centuries the most outstanding were Avicenna, who attempted to classify all existing medical knowledge, and his forerunner, Rhazes, whose shrewd clinical observations rivaled those of Hippocrates.

From the Jews, Salerno's physicians gained expert advice in the field of preventive medicine. The history of public health among the Jews goes back to about the 15th century B.C., when Moses led the Israelites out of their long captivity in Egypt. Moses had received an education from the medical priests in Egypt, and the Mosaic laws governing public health and personal hygiene proved an excellent safeguard against health hazards. Infection☞ and contagion☞ (the spreading of disease by touch) were recognized very early on and, in the event of an epidemic in an Israelite city, the *shofar*, or ram's-horn trumpet, was sounded from the city wall as a warning to avoid contact with infected persons. Then, too, the Jews learned much about the organs and organic disease through their strict religious dietary practices, which entailed the careful examination and cleaning of meat. Many leading medieval physicians were Jews.

Painting from a Persian manuscript of 1609 shows a doctor taking a patient's pulse—a method of diagnosis the Persians may have learned from the Chinese.

The Salerno medical school was a light in what, as far as health is concerned, was certainly a Dark Age. In A.D. 391 the great treasure house of Greco-Roman learning, the old and famous library at Alexandria, was destroyed, and with it much of the medical knowledge of the ancient world. The little that survived and reached Western Europe was scattered through the monasteries and dispersed among the many Orders of the Church. For almost eight centuries there was little or no advance in knowledge of the body or in the treatment of disease.

Although many of the works attributed to Hippocrates were known to the monks, his teaching that illness was not a supernatural occurrence was largely forgotten. Disease was once again regarded as a punishment for evildoing or as the work of devils, which had to be driven out by prayer, beatings, and pilgrimages to the shrines of saints, many of whom became identified with specific diseases or with parts of the body.

The towns and cities of Western Europe had grown up with a disregard for the health of their citizens, and sanitation was far cruder than it was in ancient Babylon and Imperial Rome. There was little knowledge of infection, and disease ran rife through the narrow streets and dark dwellings. Trade and war helped to spread deadly epidemics from country to country.

As great plagues swept across Europe, the people, ignorant of the cause of their suffering, felt utterly helpless and sought scapegoats on whom to blame their misery. During the Black Death that ravaged Europe in the 14th century, killing off a quarter of the population, the Jews were treated as the scapegoats and thousands of them were massacred. In the same century mass hysteria broke out in the form of the "dancing mania." Men, women, and children lost all control and danced in a frenzy, sometimes until they dropped dead in their tracks.

From the east of Europe to Flanders and Holland, the "Flagellants," a strange brotherhood who practiced self-punishment as a form of religious devotion, went about in procession, scourging each other with whips. Many ordinary people, already on the verge of hysteria, were easily persuaded to join them.

The picture, however, was not entirely dark. Many monks cultivated medicinal herb gardens, and some had acquired a smattering of scientific knowledge from the works of Galen, or from Jewish physicians who, seldom accepted anywhere for long, wandered from land to land. By the 11th century the writings of Arab alchemists had been translated into Latin and were being studied in Europe. Alchemy, at first concerned mainly with the search for the "philosopher's stone," which would transform base metals into gold, was the forerunner of chemistry.

Another redeeming feature of the Dark Ages and early Middle Ages was the growth of hospitals where, in the spirit of Christian charity, the sick were nourished and cared for. One of the hospitals was founded in London by Rahere, court jester to Henry I, who joined a religious order devoted to nursing the sick. He called it "St. Bartholomew's" after the ancient hospital-island in the river Tiber at Rome.

By the 13th century, hospitals unconnected with the Church were being provided by municipal authorities. There grew up infirmaries for the crippled, the blind, the mentally sick, and the orphaned. However, since such institutions were run without proper knowledge of hygiene or sanitation, conditions in wards often encouraged, rather than prevented, the spread of disease.

Opposite, Brueghel's 16th-century drawing of dancing maniacs. Above, scene in a 15th-century Italian hospital. Right, an 18th-century pharmacy.

Paracelsus, born when Columbus discovered the New World, stands like a Colossus astride the two worlds of superstition and science. As a young man he became the companion of miners, barbers, gypsies, and public hangmen. From them he learned more than the physicians of his time could find in books.

His real name was Theophrastus Bombast von Hohenheim, and his middle name gives us the word "bombastic," meaning loud-mouthed and self-important—as indeed he was. He was like a peacock in a field of crows, a flamboyant rebel against the dusty bookmen who believed that the Greeks had said the last word about the body and its treatment. When appointed lecturer in medicine at the University of Basel, in his native Switzerland, his first act was to make a public bonfire of classical books. He further defied tradition by lecturing in German instead of Latin, and from his own experience rather than out of books. Paracelsus transformed alchemy from an occult study into a branch of medical science, teaching that minerals as well as herbs have a part to play in healing. He advised the use of reasoning with the mentally disturbed, pointing out that "the insane and sick are our brothers."

Yet he was still a showman who practiced conjuring and indulged in astrology and the cult of salamanders. Like the witch doctors, he set out to impress his patients so that his rational prescriptions might work the better. He himself wrote: "Medicine is not merely a science but an art. . . . The character of the physician may act more powerfully upon the patient than all the drugs."

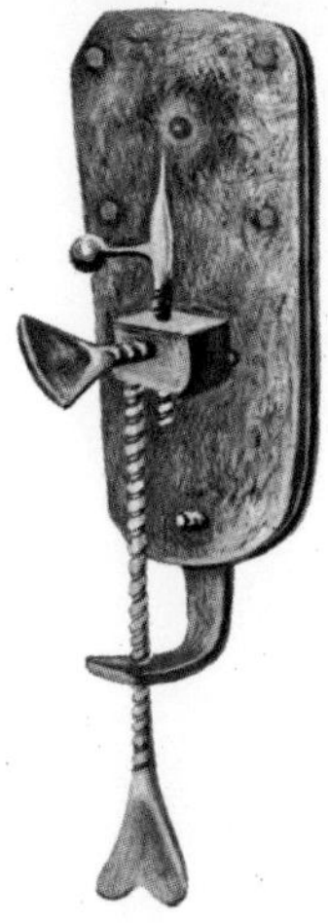

Opposite, an alchemist at work (painting of 1661). Above: left, 17th-century Londoners fleeing the plague; right, Antony van Leeuwenhoek's microscope.

During the century after Paracelsus, doctors were beginning to suspect the real nature of the "demons" of disease. Plague doctors filled the beaks of their grotesque bird-like masks with spices to purify the air they inhaled. They wore long cloaks and gauntlets and used wands to feel patients' pulses. They already guessed the invisible presence of germs.

The first step toward identifying such organisms was taken by Antony van Leeuwenhoek, a Dutchman born in 1632. Two of his fellow-countrymen had already adapted spectacle lenses capable of magnifying fleas 10 times. Leeuwenhoek developed such flea-glasses into microscopes that could enlarge 150 times.

These revealed a new world of "little animals," hundreds of thousands of which, he estimated, would scarcely equal the bulk of a coarse grain of sand. "How be it," he wrote, "that I clean my mouth with salt every day yet all the people living in our United Netherlands are not as many as the living animals I carry in my own mouth?"

Yet Leeuwenhoek's work had no immediate effect upon medical thinking. For many years most people continued to accept the ancient belief that small creatures such as lice and maggots were "spontaneously generated" from the substance in which they lived. It is hardly surprising that scientists were reluctant to believe that far smaller creatures were capable of self-reproduction.

Meanwhile the "little animals," true demons of disease, continued their deadly work. In 1812, during his unsuccessful Moscow campaign, Napoleon lost more than 90 per cent of his half-million strong Grande Armée, most of them dying of typhus, dysentery, or enteric fever. The Emperor resorted to the "Royal Touch," with which medieval monarchs had sought to cure scrofula. But the deadly "little animals" remained the only victors.

3 Death to the Demons

In Napoleon's army there was a sergeant-major who survived the epidemics and who, when his emperor went into exile, became a tanner in the Jura Mountains, which stretch along the boundary between France and Switzerland. There, in 1822, was born his son, Louis Pasteur, who was to be the standard-bearer in the war against germs.

In 1857, while Pasteur was professor of chemistry at Lille, a man who manufactured alcohol from beetroot went to him for advice; something had gone wrong with the yeasting process. With a student's simple microscope and a crude stove Pasteur began to study yeast cells; and he made a discovery—the first of many—that fermentation is a *living* process.

He showed that yeast cells, when fed on some sugary liquid in the presence of air, multiply rapidly but produce little alcohol. If air is excluded, they produce far more alcohol. The reason is that the cells need oxygen. If they can get it from the air, they do not have to extract it from the sugar. Without air, they do, and in the process they convert the sugar into alcohol.

When living organisms turn sugar into alcohol we call the process *fermentation*. But Pasteur realized that *putrefaction*—the process that makes meat or vegetables rotten—is very similar. He showed that meat will shrivel but not rot if protected from the atmosphere. If the air were free of germs, he argued, there would be no putrefaction.

He took 20 sealed flasks of broth high into the Alps. After being exposed to the pure, germ-free Alpine air, 19 samples showed no decomposition; the 20th, which did, probably contained germs before it was sealed.

Germs, Pasteur insisted, reproduce just as other living things do. Applying this knowledge, he saved the French wine industry 500,000,000 francs a year. He invented the process we call *pasteurization*—killing harmful organisms by heat.

A 19th-century cartoonist's impression of a drop of city water under a microscope.

In 1874 Pasteur received a letter from Joseph Lister, the famous British surgeon. As professor of surgery at Glasgow, Lister had been horrified by the terrible sufferings of his patients, nearly half of whom were dying from mysterious "hospital diseases." One day a professor of chemistry brought to his notice a paper Pasteur had delivered on putrefaction. Convinced that living organisms were responsible for the plight of his patients, Lister sought a way of destroying the tiny destroyers. This he found he could do by spraying wounds with carbolic acid. The era of safer surgery had begun.

Lister's letter, which acknowledged his own and humanity's debt to Pasteur, helped to turn the Frenchman from an industrial chemist into a great medical scientist. Later Pasteur identified the virus☞ responsible for chicken cholera. He also developed a successful inoculation against rabies and anthrax.

Pasteur's great German contemporary, Robert Koch, had independently discovered the germ that causes anthrax, a contagious sheep and cattle disease that also afflicts human beings. He later isolated and identified the tubercle bacillus, cause of tuberculosis☞; he also discovered the organism that produces cholera. Between them, the French soldier's son and the German country doctor had established the new science of medical bacteriology.

Lister practiced *antisepsis*☞—the destruction of germs already present; Pasteur demonstrated *asepsis*—their complete exclusion. But even before he discovered germs, some doctors had already sensed the need for such precautions. Ignaz Semmelweis in Austria and Oliver Wendell Holmes in America had scandalized their colleagues by suggesting that doctors were causing the deaths of mothers in childbirth

Louis Pasteur (1822-95), pictured with his assistants in his laboratory.

by carrying infection on hands and clothes. Semmelweis died insane, partly as a result of persecution by his colleagues, but Holmes lived to see his arguments confirmed by bacteriologists.

Today asepsis ensures that the surgeon can operate on the most delicate tissues of the body, including the brain, knowing that the risk from infection is minimal. All surgical instruments are sterilized, all doctors and nurses clad in germ-free robes, masks, and gloves.

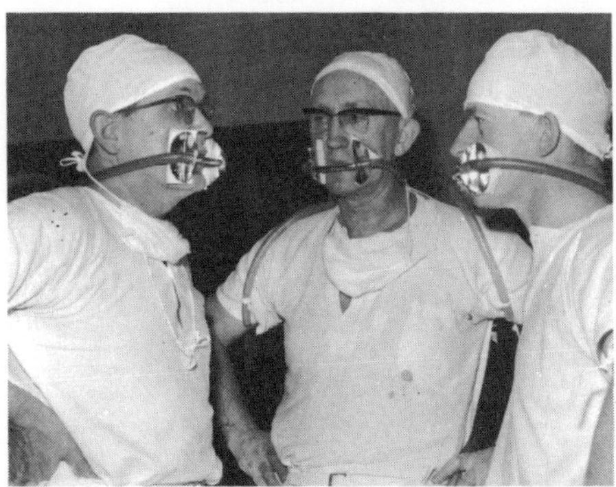

Left, sterile catgut prepared by Joseph Lister (1827-1912). Above, surgeons may now use breathing tubes to reduce risk of infection. Below, operations take place in sterile conditions.

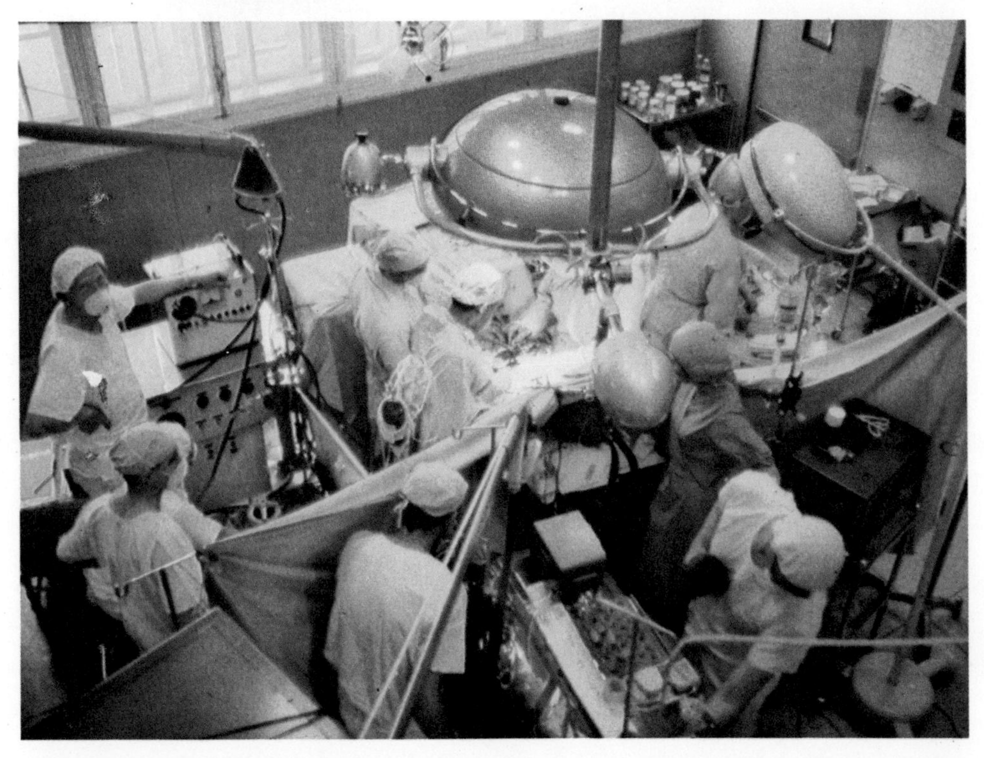

When Koch, at the height of his fame, went to Breslau to demonstrate his anthrax bacillus, the university authorities tried to hurry him past a disreputable, dye-stained bench in an otherwise immaculate laboratory. It belonged to Paul Ehrlich, a Jewish student known chiefly for his habit of neglecting lectures in order to potter around with dyes.

When Paul Ehrlich presented his doctoral thesis, however, his professors were amazed by its brilliance. Koch was so impressed that he appointed Ehrlich as his assistant. The thesis was on the staining of thin sections of body-tissue so as to make various cells and structures easily identifiable under the microscope.

Ehrlich found that certain dyes will stain one kind of tissue without affecting others. He realized that it might thus be possible to use selected dyes as messengers to carry drugs to certain tissues only. When methylene blue is injected into an animal, for example, it stains the nerves but nothing else. Ehrlich argued that it could be used to carry a narcotic☞ straight to the nerves to deaden pain.

In his work with Koch, Ehrlich also discovered that particular germs attract particular dyes. He reasoned that if he could find a dye that would be attracted by a germ but not by the body cells, he could use it to carry a substance that would destroy the germ *within the living body.* His historic success was the "magic bullet"—Salvarsan, or 606—which proved effective in the treatment of several infections, including the tropical disease yaws. It was called 606 because Ehrlich had tried 605 other dye-substances before finding the right one.

The dramatic application of Ehrlich's principle came a quarter of a century after, when the first so-called "miracle drug" appeared. This was a red dye, Prontosil, for the discovery of which Dr. Gerhard

Left, one stage in the manufacture of an antibiotic. Right, examining the mold from which the drug is made.

Domagk was later awarded a Nobel prize. It was the first of the sulfonamides☞, the precision drugs that doctors can now direct against many specific infections. The sulfonamides are chemically similar to the substances on which the germs normally live, but the vital part needed by the germs for survival and multiplication has been replaced by something else. Without that vital "fraction" the germs cannot live.

Seven years before Domagk's discovery, Professor Alexander Fleming, returning from holiday to his laboratory in London, found that in his absence a piece of fluff had drifted under the cover of a dish containing a colony of germs he had been cultivating. Before discarding the dish as spoiled, he looked at it more closely. Thus penicillin was discovered.

The fluff was actually a mold, and around it was a clear circle in which no germs were growing. Fleming realized the mold was exuding a substance that was destroying them. He grew the mold and applied this substance, in crude form, to surface sores. He obtained good results—but no better than those obtained with other germicides.

Ten years later, Ernest Chain, a German-born doctor, working with Professor Howard Florey at Oxford, read an account of Fleming's work. With a perception heightened by the success of the sulfonamides in killing germs within the living body, he saw a new significance in Fleming's discovery. Florey and Chain together developed penicillin into the great destroyer of germs within the body that we know today.

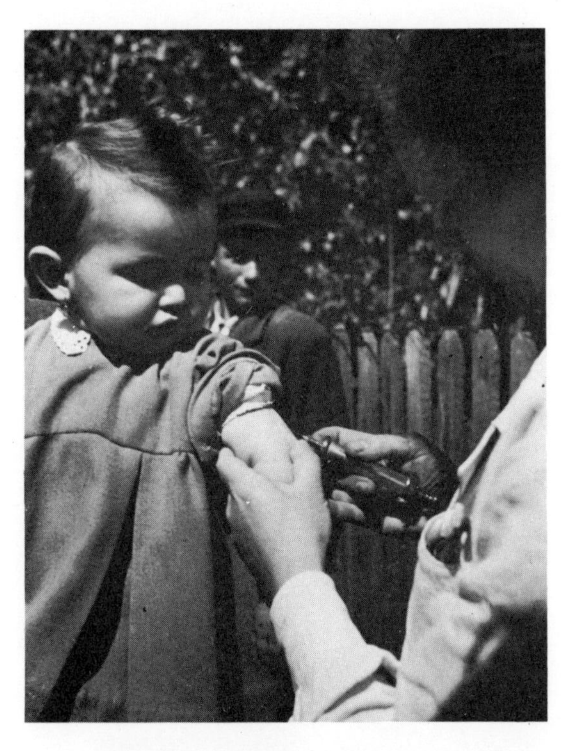

Above, a Yugoslav boy has his first penicillin injection. Right, laboratory model of a penicillin spore.

It is good to have the cure for a disease but it is far better not to have the disease—to be *immune* from it. Most people have a natural immunity☞ to a surprising number of diseases; otherwise we should all be continually infected by one or another of the germs that beset us. Usually we owe our immunity to the fact that we have actually had the disease in a very mild form, often without noticing it.

In ancient China and India, physicians noticed that people who survived smallpox were usually immune from a second attack. They therefore began to practice *inoculation*☞, which meant taking some of the infective material from a person suffering from a mild form of smallpox and introducing it into the bodies of those wishing to be protected. The operation was risky because a form of smallpox mild to one individual may be dangerous to another.

By the early part of the 18th century, inoculation with human smallpox had long been practiced in Turkey, and Lady Mary Wortley Montagu, wife of the British Ambassador to Turkey, had herself and her son inoculated in this way. The disease was then so common that even the plainest woman was considered a beauty if she were not pockmarked. It is not, therefore, surprising that other English people were willing to follow Lady Mary's example. That was around 1718, and this form of inoculation doubtless prepared the way for the less hazardous practice of *vaccination.*

In 1796 Edward Jenner, a British doctor living in Gloucestershire, noticed that a dairymaid, Sarah Nelmes, had a cowpox rash on her arm. According to local tradition, people who had had cowpox, a comparatively harmless disease contracted from cows, rarely caught smallpox, and Jenner believed it might be possible to take advantage of this to prevent the spread of the more dangerous disease. He therefore took some of the matter from the dairymaid's arm and injected it into the arm of a small boy, James Phipps, who suffered nothing worse than a sore that scarred and quickly healed. Two months later Jenner took the drastic step of injecting him with virulent human smallpox. The boy remained perfectly well.

Since Jenner's time vaccines have provided protection against a wide range of deadly diseases. BCG, for example, has been used by the United Nations agencies to protect tens of millions against tuberculosis. This "bacillus Calmette-Guérin" is named after the two Frenchmen who bred a very mild form of the tubercle bacillus that is injected alive to provide immunity. The Salk vaccine, developed for polio protection by Dr. Jonas Salk of Pittsburgh, USA, consists of a virus

Left, Sarah Nelmes's cowpox rash. In 1796, Jenner used pus from the sores to make the first vaccine against smallpox. Opposite, a cartoon of 1904 depicting French chemists Pierre and Marie Curie, discoverers of radium.

Imp

that, though it is killed before being injected, nevertheless causes the body to react as it would to an extremely mild attack of polio.

When these mild disease-germs enter the body, they provoke antibodies☞—chemicals that try to repel them. The antibodies succeed, and remain there as a kind of garrison, ready to repel a future attack by the same type of germ.

In the bitterness of the Franco-Prussian War (1870–71) a French scientist dared to suggest that the Prussians were not Teutons but descendants of Attila's Mongols. This so enraged the German pathologist Rudolf Virchow that he had six million Prussian schoolchildren examined. Their skulls were measured, their bone formation studied, their teeth examined, one hair pulled from each head and classified. He proved scientifically that they were of true Germanic stock.

This was typical of the thoroughness that made Virchow one of the greatest figures in medical history. With better microscopes, and new ways of dyeing body tissues so as to distinguish them by color, Virchow discovered the cell-structure of the body and studied the behavior of cells. The body, he declared, was like a state made up of citizens—the cells. If cells were sick or in revolt, the body-state was sick or in revolt. Health was the harmony, and disease the disharmony, of the cells.

Among Virchow's "anarchic" cells are those of cancer☞. Cancer cells, far from being sickly, are stronger and multiply more rapidly than the normal cells around them. They are "rebels" in the body-state and the body has no means within itself of coping with them. There

was little hope of quelling them by external means until the discovery of the element radium, in 1898.

In 1896 Henri Becquerel, a French professor, had discovered that uranium gives off rays similar to Röntgen's X rays☞. In Paris at that time was Marie Curie, a refugee from Poland. She had married Pierre Curie, of the School of Physics and Chemistry, and had a baby daughter, Irène, who later became, like her parents, a Nobel prize winner. In addition to her household duties, Marie decided to work for a degree, and chose as the subject of her research the Becquerel rays.

In an effort to find out whether other substances had the peculiar property of giving out rays, or "radioactivity," as she called it, she examined every known element. She found that the ore pitchblende is far more radioactive than can be explained by the radioactive uranium in it. Pitchblende must thus contain an element or elements, hitherto unknown, more radioactive than uranium.

After years of work, in which she and her husband melted and stirred tons of pitchblende in a great caldron, Marie succeeded in isolating two such "new" elements. One she named *polonium*, after her native Poland, and the other *radium*.

It was soon discovered that the rays from radium can arrest the growth of cancerous cells, though not without danger to healthy tissues. Had the Curies patented their radium-extraction process they might then have made a fortune. "No," they said, "if radium is to be used for the treatment of disease, it is impossible for us to take advantage of suffering humanity." And they cheerfully mounted their bicycles and rode off to the woods of Clamart.

Radium has now largely been replaced by cobalt 60, a metal treated in atomic reactors. Other radioactive isotopes, in the discovery of which Irène Curie and her husband Frédéric Joliot played a vital part, are also used in the treatment of certain forms of cancer. These by-products of atomic energy are used to radiate internally in a cancer growth. They can also detect such a growth. A *scintiscanner* picks up rays from injected isotopes and builds up a picture in which the growth appears darkest because it absorbs most radioactivity.

Medical science is still seeking chemicals that will "starve" the greedy cancer cells without doing any harm to the normal cells.

The history of medicine rightly highlights the names of a few great men and women who have made original contributions to the science and art of healing; but in the day-to-day war against disease and injury it is the great army of "unknown" medical practitioners—the doctors and nurses in your town and every town—who are in the front firing line. It is they who ascertain the patient's needs and call up the resources of medical science to meet them.

Children in China line up for BCG vaccination against tuberculosis.

The family doctor's day usually begins with an early-morning surgery. Most of the patients in his crowded waiting room need nothing more than a bottle of cough-mixture, a week's respite from overwork, or perhaps a few reassuring words. But one or two—the boy with a persistent sore throat, the woman who is mysteriously losing too much weight—may need hospital treatment. In any event the doctor will want to seek the opinion of his colleagues about them.

Not long ago, the general practitioner working in a small town was an isolated figure, relying almost wholly on his own experience and ability. Today, by regularly exchanging views and case-notes with fellow doctors, he adds to his own efficiency as well as to theirs. When, on his morning round, he assures a mother that her sick child will be

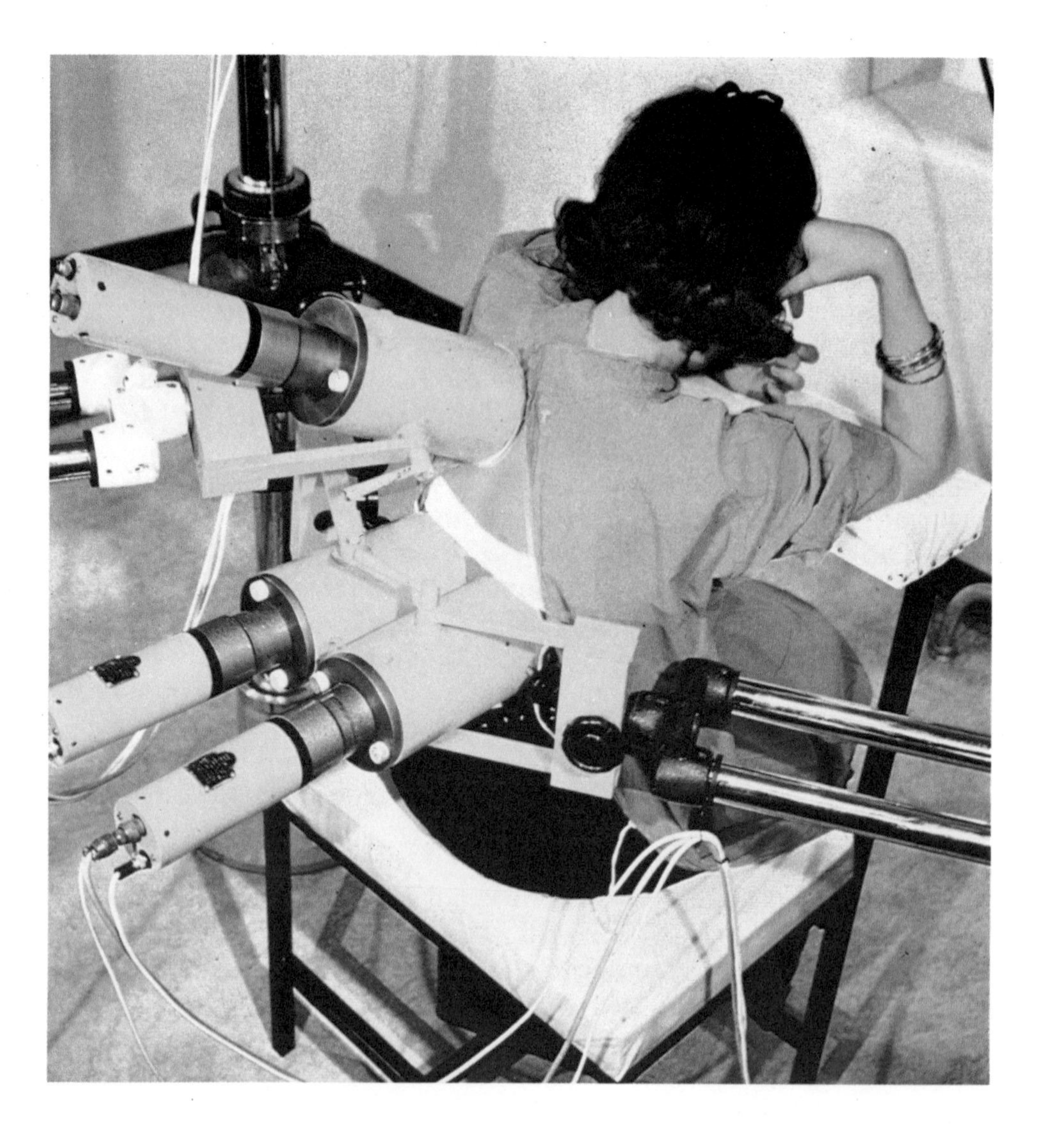

Radioisotopes, injected into the bloodstream, will show the rate of flow through different organs. Here, detectors are in position over the kidneys and heart.

all right, it *will* be all right. He knows that from their common fund of experience, upon which he and his colleagues can draw.

When he has to deal with a road accident, he can rely upon the cooperation of trained first-aid workers. When he accompanies the casualty to hospital, he himself cooperates with the casualty officer. In diagnosing the complaints of his own patients, he can enlist the help of the hospital's X-ray department. But when disease, accident, or birth demands immediate medical attention in the small night hours, it is he alone who must leave his bed and answer the call. Being a doctor is not just a profession—it is a vocation. And the same is true of nursing.

It has not always been so. In the early 19th century, nursing was far removed from the kindly ministrations of the devout medieval nuns

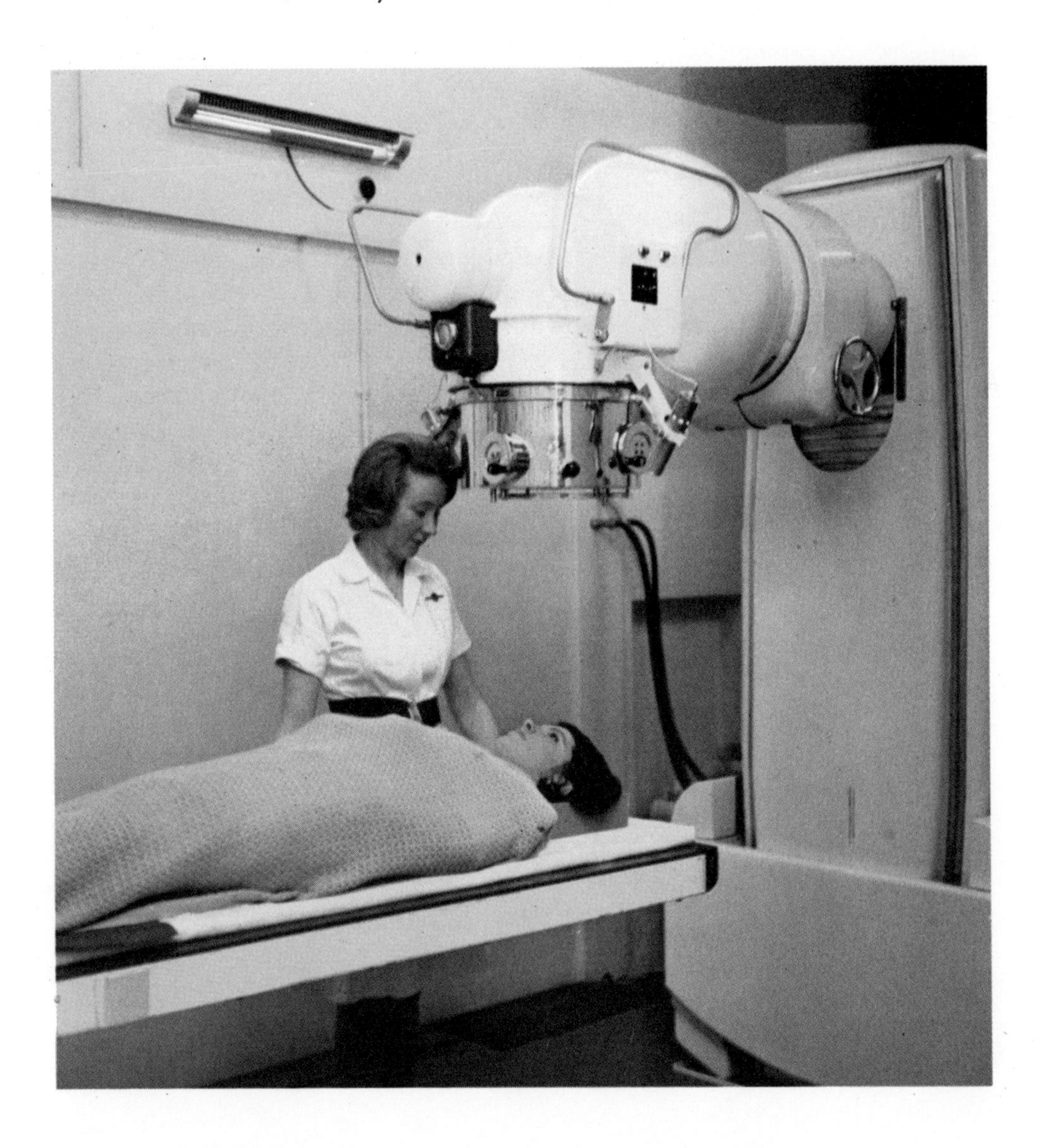

Using the radioactive isotope cobalt 60 to treat a cancer growth. Rays are focused exactly on cancer area, to minimize the risk of damage to normal cells.

who, though without medical training, had tended the bodies and souls of the sick. It had become a low, menial trade, practiced by degraded slatterns like Dickens's gin-sodden Sairey Gamp. No self-respecting woman would have dreamed of becoming a nurse.

Not until the middle of the century did the position begin to improve. At that time a wealthy German pastor, Theodor Fliedner, and his wife were running a hospital where they trained nursing deaconesses. An aristocratic Englishwoman, Florence Nightingale, visited the Fliedners, and was so impressed that she took a course there.

In March 1854, Britain became involved in war with Russia. Unlike their French allies, who had nuns to tend the sick and wounded, the British had to rely largely on untrained medical orderlies.

In October of that year, Florence Nightingale went to the Crimean battlefront, taking with her a small party of hand-picked nurses. Working sometimes with the help, often despite the hindrance, of the authorities, she rapidly took the control of nursing out of the hands of the military and made women responsible. By sheer perseverance and force of character she overcame the apathy and opposition of officialdom and succeeded in improving the appalling sanitary conditions of the military hospitals, so bringing about a tremendous decrease of deaths from disease. But to the ordinary soldier she was something much more than a hospital reformer: she was "the Lady of the Lamp," going around the dark wards at night, bringing comfort to the sick.

By her own example she changed nursing from a despised trade to a noble profession. On her return to England, she established a school for nurses at St. Thomas's Hospital, London. There she imposed rigorous discipline and arduous training. Even the uniform—the starched cap, the apron, the severe gown—played an essential part in the process; so did the "indignities" of the probationers' training and the stern

Above, Florence Nightingale, pictured with wounded soldiers in Scutari hospital. Opposite, Kenyan student nurses learn anatomy—part of every nurse's training.

discipline imposed by the matron. The immaculate nurse was the answer to Sairey Gamp. Genteel ladies had to learn the humility of handling slops, and that a hospital ward was no place for the fastidious. Every nurse had to observe strict obedience to medical instructions.

Today, exacting demands for medical qualifications have been added to training in the Nightingale tradition, for in many fields the work of the nurse is an essential supplement to the work of the doctor. The surgeon, carrying out a delicate operation, must rely implicitly on the experience of the theatre sister; the anesthetist, on his nurse-assistant; the physician, on the ward-nurses who administer his treatment.

Nurses have become specialists in midwifery, children's illnesses, or care of the old. The ranks of the profession also include X-ray technicians, physiotherapists☞, experts in remedial exercises, and other medical auxiliaries. There are home nurses, industrial nurses, and health visitors; and there are international nurses—sister-tutors who, under primitive, often dangerous, and always adventurous conditions, go out to underdeveloped countries to train others in the care of the sick. Through their efforts and those of the agencies they serve, such as the World Health Organization, even the formerly illiterate midwives are responding to training in modern hygienic practices. In countries where, by tradition, women seldom see much of the world outside their own homes, nursing training is often the first step toward independence.

The problems facing the doctors and nurses of today are very different from those of Florence Nightingale's time. Many infectious diseases are now almost wiped out, but as fever wards empty, casualty wards fill.

Accidents in the home, on the roads, and in the factories increase year by year. The annual figures for road deaths and injuries alone are as big as the casualty lists of a major battle. And the Machine Age takes its toll in other ways too.

True, muscles are less frequently subjected to the stress of grueling manual toil; but the nervous system is increasingly under the stress of relentless time-pressure, distracting noise, nameless fears and worries. All too often the individual finds himself unable to keep up the pace, unequal to the struggle of modern living. The regular rhythm of sleep and waking is broken; sleeping pills become a commonplace, and the demand for "tranquilizers" grows. Mental and nervous disorders increase. Many doctors believe that degenerative diseases, such as "hardening of the arteries" and certain heart complaints, formerly common only among the old, are increasing among the middle-aged.

The prevention of accidents and stress diseases is not primarily a medical but a social problem. But doctors have the task of patching and repairing. The surgeon can "repair" injured limbs, operate on damaged organs, cure some types of blindness. The plastic surgeon can remodel a disfigured face. The surgical engineer can devise ingenious substitutes for missing limbs. The physician, with new drugs and modern treatments, can reduce the ill-effects of shock☞ and internal injury. The psychologist can help people to readjust themselves, and the occupational therapist, by prescribing the right activities, can help mentally as well as physically sick people.

Not all physical defects, of course, result from accidents. There have always been infants born blind, deformed, or deaf and dumb, and there have always been people who became paralyzed or crippled as a result of disease.

As far back as 1836, Louis Braille, a blind teacher of the blind, used a system of embossed points that enabled a sightless person to read a book by the sense of touch. Today his system, and others like it, are supplemented by "talking books"—sound recordings covering a wide range of literature. Not long ago almost the only way blind people could earn a living was by basket-making; now they are trained for many different trades and professions.

At one time, a child born deaf had little chance of learning to speak, since he had no sound-pattern of speech to copy. Today, electronic hearing aids can overcome many forms of deafness.

Top, lessons in lip movements, and in the hand alphabet, enable the deaf to "hear." Center: left, tape-recording books to provide talking libraries for the blind; right, a radio circuit printed in raised dots for the benefit of blind electricians. Lower, an artificial arm helps a disabled person to teach.

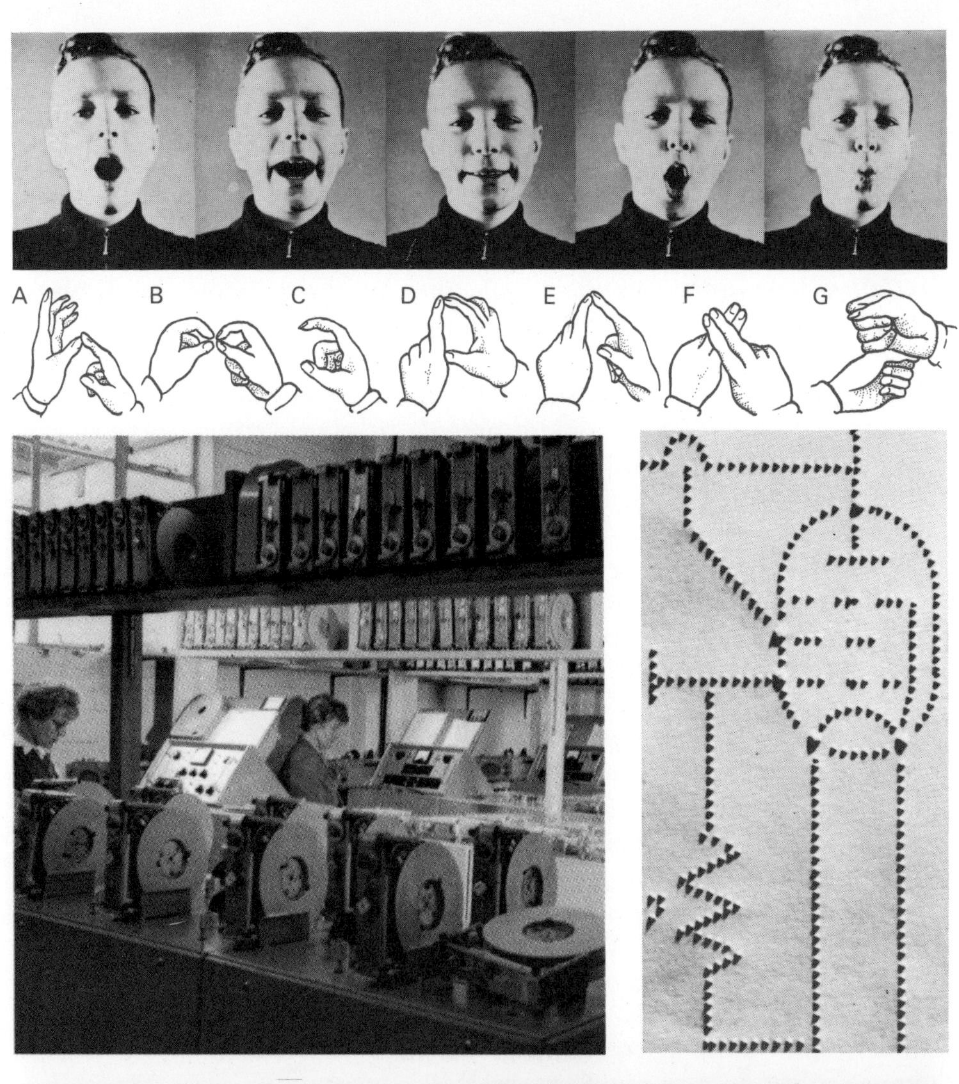
A
B
C
D
E
F
G

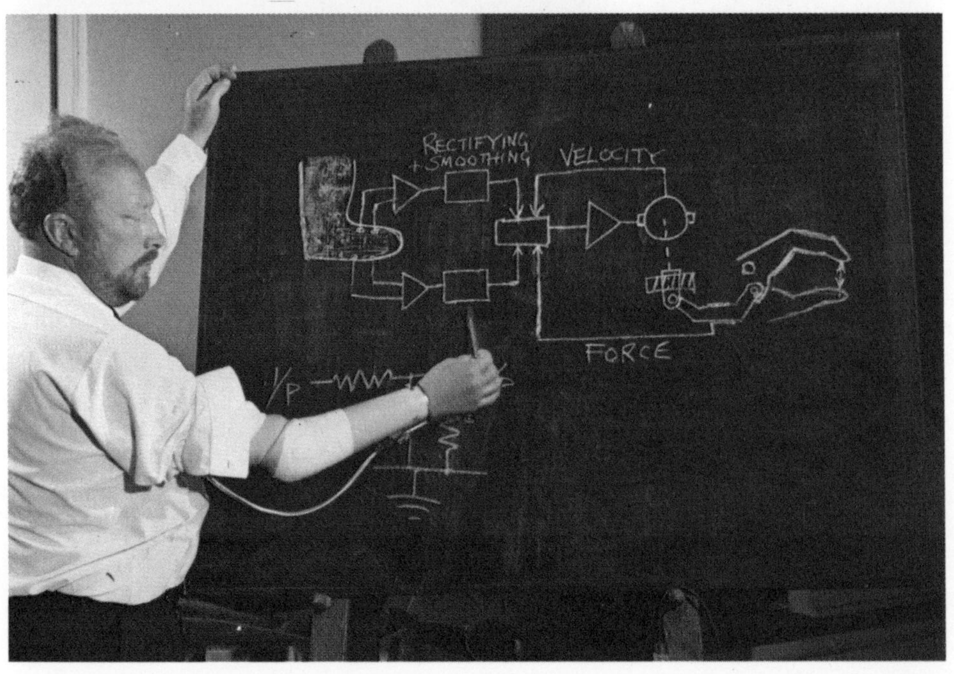
RECTIFYING
+ SMOOTHING
VELOCITY
FORCE
I/P

A thousand years ago, the great hospital at Damascus provided treatment without fee for everyone, from the sultan to his poorest subject. Even wayfarers, tired only in body or in spirit, were given beds and nourishment—young chicken, sherbet, and sweetmeats. But, after three days, they were prescribed an unpleasant medicine as a hint that they had outstayed their welcome. In the religious hospitals of the Middle Ages, treatment, without adequate medical knowledge, could be little more than kindness.

But in time hospitals became great teaching establishments, as well as places for the care of the sick. Eminent doctors gave their services free, teaching students in the wards, and learning much themselves from their opportunities for clinical observation. In the 19th century general hospitals were supplemented by special ones, devoted to particular complaints. There, physicians became more expert in diagnosing and treating a certain limited range of diseases, surgeons more expert in operating on particular parts of the body. This specialization encouraged medical and surgical skill, but it often made doctors regard the patient as an interesting case, rather than as a whole man.

To counteract this tendency, modern planning aims at bringing together many specialized departments within the framework of a single organization. One of the most famous institutions of this kind is the Mayo Clinic at Rochester, Minnesota. This had its beginnings in the 1880s, when three notable American surgeons, a father and his two sons, all worked at the small and recently established St. Mary's Hospital in Rochester. The father, William Worrall Mayo, and the two sons, William and Charles, each specialized in a different field of surgery. News of the successes they achieved by working together spread quickly and soon the group partnership of specialists developed into a world-famous institution, combining hospital treatment with surgery, teaching, and research.

One has only to think of the skills placed at the patient's disposal to understand why it costs more to offer him a hospital bed than to house him in the most luxurious hotel. There are not only highly trained physicians, surgeons, nurses, almoners, technicians, and orderlies to attend to his needs; the workers in the hospital laundry, who ensure that linen is completely sterile, and the kitchen staff, who provide meals suited to his particular needs, contribute to his treatment as certainly as those whose work lies in the operating theatres, the X-ray department, the pathology laboratory, or the rehabilitation departments.

Within the one single institution there are also casualty departments, outpatient clinics, maternity wards, and geriatric☞ wards where the aged are cared for. Many enlightened hospitals also have psychiatric wards, where the mentally ill can rightly feel that no distinction is made between them and the physically sick.

Today, improved communications and transport often make it possible to take the hospital to the patient, rather than the patient to the hospital.

In a cabin in the far north of Canada, a woman lay desperately ill. The only "doctor" was a Mountie; the only equipment, his first-aid book and medicine chest. Neither the book nor the chest could provide the answer to her complaint. The Mountie started the engine-generator of his radio transmitter and called the nearest hospital—1500 miles away. The surgeon he contacted took a grave view: only an immediate operation would save the patient.

"Have you some fresh safety razor-blades?" he asked. "All right, sterilize them. Now, write down these instructions: On her skin, draw a circle six inches in diameter. . . . Yes, of course a fountain pen will do. Draw a line vertically from the center. Make your first incision along that line. . . ." And so, by radio, the surgeon directed an operation that saved the woman's life. When the aircraft arrived to take her to hospital, it was not needed. She had a rather inelegant scar but there were no complications.

Layout of a modern hospital unit, showing its many specialized departments.

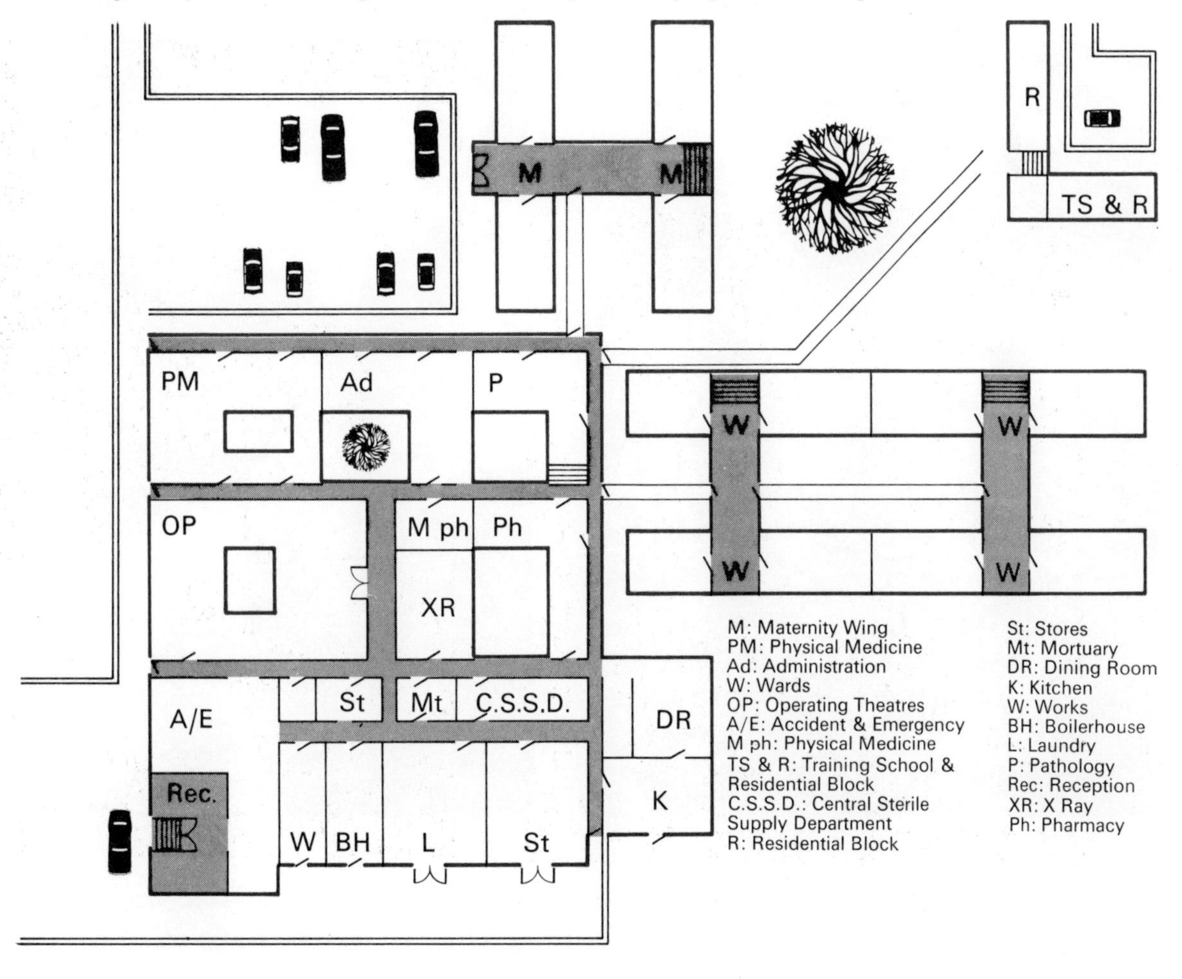

Radio and aviation also enable sick or injured people in remote places to summon the doctor quickly. In the islands of Scotland, the interior of Australia, the vast emptiness of the Northwest Territories of Canada, the remote parts of the United States, or the jungle clearings of Asia, the "flying doctor" has become a familiar figure. Some doctors pilot their own light aircraft as a matter of routine, just as their city colleague drives his own car. Where a plane cannot land easily, it is not uncommon for doctors or nurses to drop by parachute, or for a sling to be lowered from a helicopter to pick up the patient. Sometimes a plane is fitted out as an ambulance, or flying clinic.

A few years ago such "mercy flights" made front-page headlines. Today, unless the patient is an airman lost for weeks, or a seaman on a ship in stormy seas, we seldom hear of them; they are a normal part of life in the "wide open spaces."

When fishing fleets set out for the foggy Grand Banks of Newfoundland or the fishing grounds of the Arctic, they are often accompanied by hospital ships equipped to carry out major operations. In Borneo, hospital boats—native craft fitted with outboard motors—regularly push

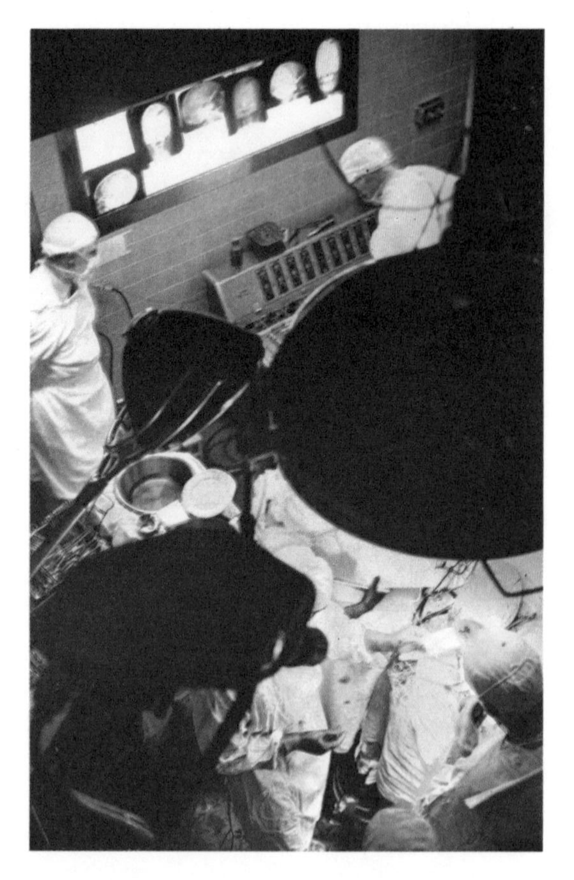

Left, medical students see an operation relayed on closed-circuit television. Right, the camera in the operating theatre registers the surgeon's every move.

their way through mangrove swamps and up crocodile-infested rivers; the tribesmen know when to expect them, and assemble on the river banks for treatment. In the Arctic, snowmobiles, fitted with skis and caterpillar tracks, take medical teams on their rounds of the frozen wastes. By jeep or by elephant, doctors and nurses penetrate the jungles of Asia, carrying tiger guns as an essential part of their equipment.

Taking the hospital to the patient is not confined to isolated areas. In big cities mobile X-ray units, designed to detect the first onset of tuberculosis, travel around like gigantic tradesmen's vans. In Holland "mental first-aid" teams visit the mentally ill in their own homes.

Apart from the fact that many people respond best to medical treatment at home, hospitals are expensive institutions, and beds should be reserved for those most in need. Many beds are still occupied by the "chronic aged," who need regular care and attention rather than skilled medical treatment. Today there is a tendency to treat such people at home. Well-planned, appetizing meals are taken to them; nurses visit them regularly; specialists see them at intervals; and often good neighbors take it in turn to keep them company.

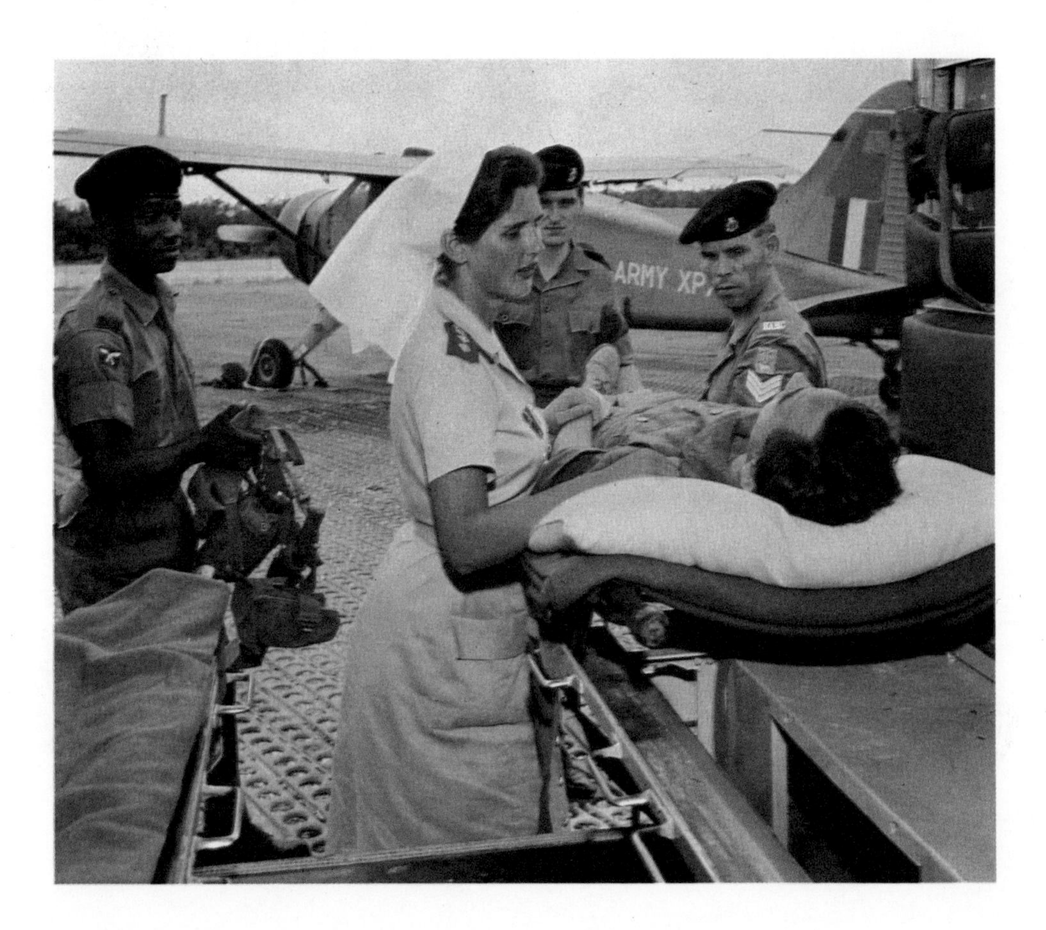

A British Army nurse in the Yemen rushes a casualty to the hospital.

4 Cooperation and Control

We live in a world that is probably healthier than at any other time in history. But deadly diseases still exist and they are still capable of spreading. Today disease can travel with the speed of sound, if an insect carrying it should stow away on a jet-propelled plane. A typhus-infested louse, brushed off the rags of a beggar in an Eastern bazaar, may land a few hours later in New York. Plague may have lain dormant for years behind the battlements of the Himalayas, but an aircraft may bring it to Europe in a day.

The speed of modern travel has so shrunk distance-in-time that a plague spot thousands of miles away is almost next door. Without an effective world system of epidemic control, no community would be really safe. Fortunately, such a system does exist, and its hub is the Epidemiological Division of the World Health Organization. WHO, a specialized agency of the United Nations, was set up in 1948 to win international cooperation in the cause of better health, and in a few years its badge, which includes the ancient sign of the Aesculapian serpent, has become known throughout the world.

Disease control is not a new problem. As long ago as 1403 the doges of Venice made it compulsory for travelers from the disease-ridden Levant to be held in isolation for 40 days—*quaranta giorni*, whence comes the word *quarantine*. But as travel became faster, people would no longer submit to such delays. One obstacle in the way of international agreement on epidemic control during the 19th century was the fact that mercantile nations objected to interference with trade movements. We can imagine what today's air-traveler, who resents even the brief delay at the airport medical checkpoint, would have to say about a 40-day detention!

Travelers—and disease—may travel with the speed of sound, but radio messages travel with the speed of light, and it is this fact that enables WHO to exercise control with a minimum of inconvenience.

Daumier's etching shows a house marked with the 17th-century sign of the plague.

Opposite, the Geneva headquarters of the World Health Organization. Upper, undernourished African children, some suffering from protein deficiency (kwash-iorkor), are treated at a WHO research center in the Congo. Lower, an old lady's treatment at a WHO psychiatric hospital includes a walk with the nurse.

Every day WHO broadcasts an epidemic bulletin in Morse, from its headquarters in Geneva. That bulletin is based on up-to-the-minute reports from all parts of the world, of any appearance, anywhere, of pestilential diseases—cholera, plague, yellow fever, relapsing fever, smallpox, and typhus. In emergencies it includes notifications of influenza☞, polio, and other diseases. Captains and ships' doctors also notify the organization when they have any suspected cases of epidemic disease on board. With eight transmitters in Geneva and a network of others in America, southeast Asia, and elsewhere, WHO ensures that not only public health authorities in every country, but also every seaport and every airport, are kept informed.

With this information, medical officers are on the alert. If a ship or an aircraft has called at a place where dangerous infections have been discovered, special vigilance is exercised. If the craft carries a suspected case of infection, the health authorities at the next port of call stand ready to remove the "suspect" to hospital, and to vaccinate or isolate anyone else who may have been in contact with him.

Under the code of International Sanitary Regulations drawn up by WHO and accepted by most governments, many threatened epidemics can thus be arrested at an early stage. A quarantine can be quickly imposed; and just as quickly withdrawn when danger has passed. Regulations demanding inoculations☞ or vaccinations☞ can be enforced or relaxed, according to the state of the disease-map.

This is only one of the numerous activities of WHO. It also coordinates the work of public health laboratories, recommends international standards for drugs, helps in the rehabilitation of handicapped children, and in many other ways mobilizes the medical forces of the world.

In 1535, when the French explorer Cartier sailed to Newfoundland, many of his crew fell ill with scurvy, a disease then often fatal. The Indians provided a potion made from the needles of the spruce tree. "All the doctors of Montpellier and Louvain," he wrote, "could not have done so much in a year as that tree did in six days." Some two centuries later, Captain Cook kept his crews free from scurvy by giving them fresh fruit juices. These later became compulsory rations on British ships, and gave rise to a nickname for the British—"Limeys." Yet no one then realized that scurvy is caused by the lack of some essential in diet.

During the 19th century, chemists made the first baby foods, containing everything they believed at the time to be necessary—carbohydrates, fats, and proteins. Many babies who were fed on them died of infantile scurvy. Chemists did not yet know about vitamin C—a substance found in fruit juices.

The science of nutrition did not properly begin until the close of the 19th century. Its pioneers were Christiaan Eijkman, a Dutchman; Sir Frederick Gowland Hopkins, an Englishman; and Casimir Funk, a Pole. Eijkman was investigating a deadly epidemic in the prisons of Java, supposedly a germ disease. He noticed that some fowls in the prison yard had the same type of symptoms as the human prisoners. Both were fed on polished rice, and he thought the infection was being carried by the food. Then an officious jailer suddenly insisted that polished rice was too good for poultry: in future they should be given unmilled rice. To Eijkman's surprise, the fowls recovered, while the prisoners still had the disease—beriberi. Thus vitamin B was discovered—a substance present in the bran, but missing from the milled rice. Lack of it caused the disease.

It was Hopkins who, after proving that carbohydrates, fats, and proteins—even with mineral salts added—do not form a complete diet, started the search for "accessory food factors." It was Funk who discovered that yeast, as well as rice husks, can cure beriberi, and who coined the words *vitamins*☞, or *vitamines*, as he spelt it.

Today the alphabet of vitamins, many of which can be produced artificially, is growing rapidly. They are powerful chemicals that the bodv must absorb in order to function properly. A watchglassful of artificial vitamin D, which cures (or prevents) rickets, is enough to provide one day's dose for a million children. Doses of two millionths of a gram of vitamin B_{12} can restore the normal supply of red blood cells in a person suffering from pernicious anemia☞.

Knowledge of vitamins enables doctors to cure complaints that were a mystery 50 years ago. Even more important, it enables governments and international agencies throughout the world to conduct campaigns to persuade people to eat foods that will *prevent* deficiency diseases.

A baby suffering from malnutrition awaits treatment at a hospital in Brazil.

Prevention is always better than cure. Like the romantic poets, doctors would prefer us all to be shepherds and shepherdesses in Arcadia, with abundant fresh air, fresh water, and fresh food, and with plenty of pleasant exercise. Then, providing we did not get rheumatism from dancing barefoot in the dew, our bodies would have a chance to be completely healthy.

Instead, many of our cities, especially those that expanded rapidly during the Steam Age, have grown haphazardly, huddling millions of people together in congested buildings, thickening the air with smoke, polluting the waters, and permitting food to be contaminated with germs. People have to struggle to work through traffic jams or crowded subways; they earn their living in a hubbub of noise and distractions;

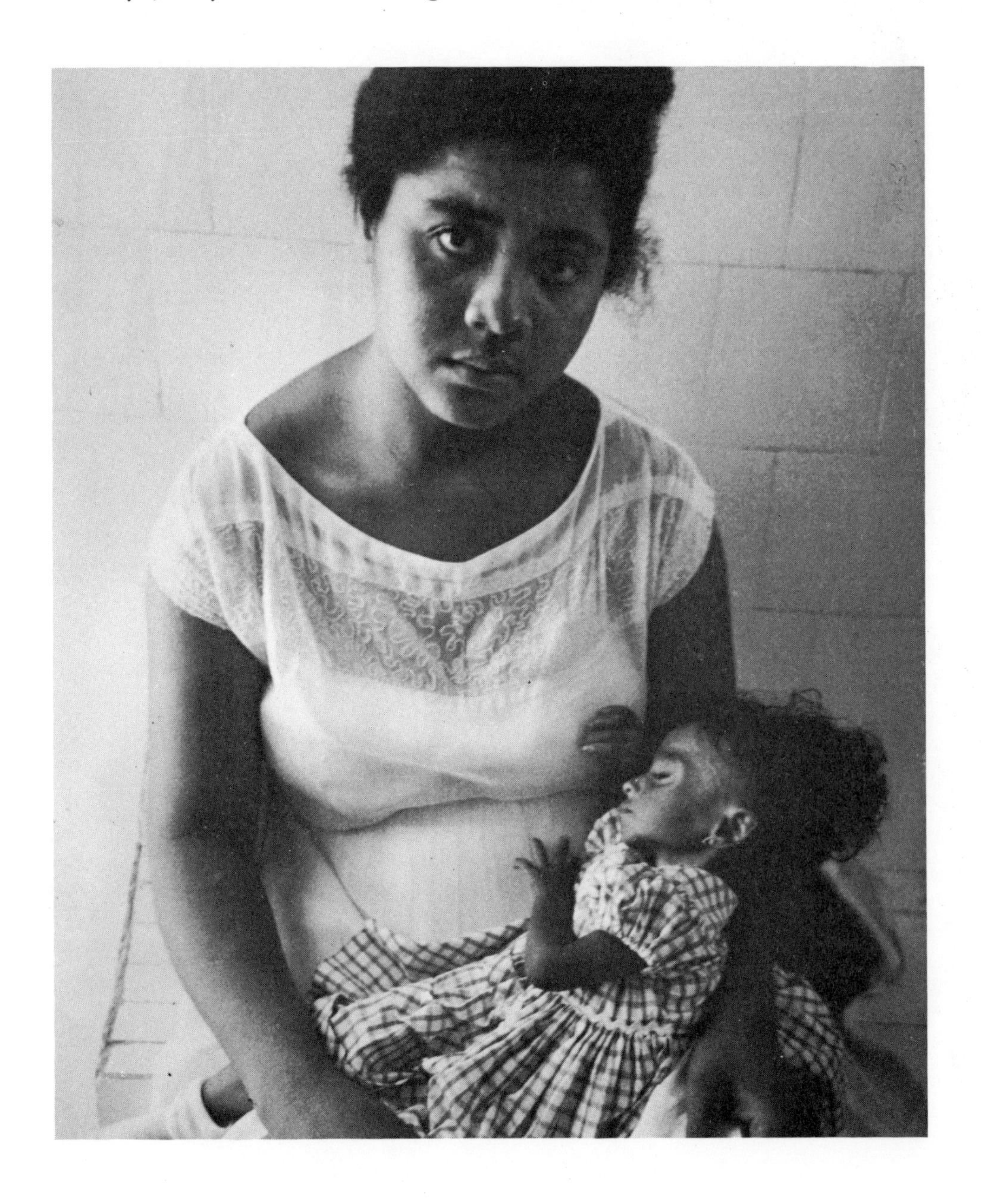

Town-planning at Crawley, England, lets fresh air and sunshine into buildings.

they spend much of their leisure in crowded places of amusement where there is little rest for overworked nerves.

There is no return to Arcadia, but medical knowledge and modern enlightenment can bring doctors, artists, architects, educators, and town-planners together to produce healthy living conditions. Towns need not be drab, dirty, smoky, noisy. Buildings can reach up and spread out to give more fresh air and sunshine. Green spaces can provide "lungs" for our cities and playgrounds for the people. Roads can be built to carry traffic under or over residential areas.

Schools, offices, shops, and factories can be brightly painted, sound-muted, sun-catching, and well ventilated. Homes, even in the heart of a city where they cannot have gardens, can have brightness and freshness and comfort. City dwellers cannot drink from the running stream or live on berries gathered from the hedgerows, but they can have purified water and safe food. The rapid increase in the use of refrigeration, deep-freeze, and canning, is already cutting out the risks of contamination while still preserving the goodness of our food. Civic authorities ensure clean water supplies.

As civilization advances, man has to compromise with his environment, using his ingenuity and wisdom to redress the balance between what is desirable and what is unavoidable in city life. Often he learns only from his mistakes—from the slums, the smoke, and the waterborne diseases that increased with the Industrial Revolution.

During this century he has created new difficulties for himself. He has means of transport faster than ever before but he has allowed traffic congestion to slow down his cities to the pace of the horse-and-buggy days. Today atomic energy offers abundance of clean power, but public health requires safeguards against radiation hazards. This time we can avoid the risks by applying what we already know.

Modern homes for the aged provide expert care, comfort, and scope for hobbies.

From the beginning, man has waged a ceaseless battle to adapt himself to his environment, or his environment to his own needs. It is reasonably certain that he originated in a warm climate where, without a natural covering of fur or feathers, he could still survive. Only when he discovered how to clothe himself in the pelts of animals and how to light fires could he face life in colder regions.

Many thousands of years ago, possibly before the Bering Strait separated Asia from America, Asian men wandered northward into the tundra and crossed into the Western Hemisphere. There they learned that the Arctic presents dangers of heat, as well as of cold. Had they wrapped themselves tightly in furs, they might have stewed in their own body-steam, and died when it froze. Instead, they made loose-fitting fur garments to give body-ventilation.

At all times man has trained his body for feats of endurance far beyond anything normal living would impose. And as science has discovered more about the workings of the human body its endurance has been steadily extended. In diving suits and bathyscaphes, man has descended to ocean depths where pressures would crush his unprotected body. At lesser depths, skin divers with breathing apparatus on their backs, "windows" to protect their eyes, and flippers on their feet, have joined the schools of fish. On the surface of the ocean, one man, at least, has traveled thousands of miles, living mainly on plankton. Carrying oxygen with him, man has climbed the world's highest mountains and ascended into the rarefied air of the stratosphere. He has broken through the sound barrier, traveling at speeds that should destroy him.

"Aviation medicine," which studies how to accustom men to stratosphere and high-speed flying, has now led to "space medicine," which works to train and equip those who are venturing far beyond all the known environments of our earth. Human beings are spun in chairs revolving at a speed that simulates the acceleration of a rocket, in which the forces of gravity can make a 150-lb. man weigh 2550 lb. As a result of such experiments space suits have been devised to help keep blood circulating at a safe rate under such abnormal conditions. "Radiation medicine," which has grown up with the release of atomic energy, is rapidly learning how to protect us from materials that give off rays harmful to living things. Just as men in asbestos suits can venture into a blazing furnace, so men clothed in special plastic materials can venture into the unseen rays of the "atom furnace"—the nuclear reactor. Thus today medical science helps man both to master natural environments and to live in new environments of his own making.

Upper, American astronaut Edward H. White makes his spectacular 21-minute space "walk" during the third orbit of his Gemini flight (1965). Lower, an engineer works 205 feet under the ocean, in the U.S. deep-sea module Sealab II.

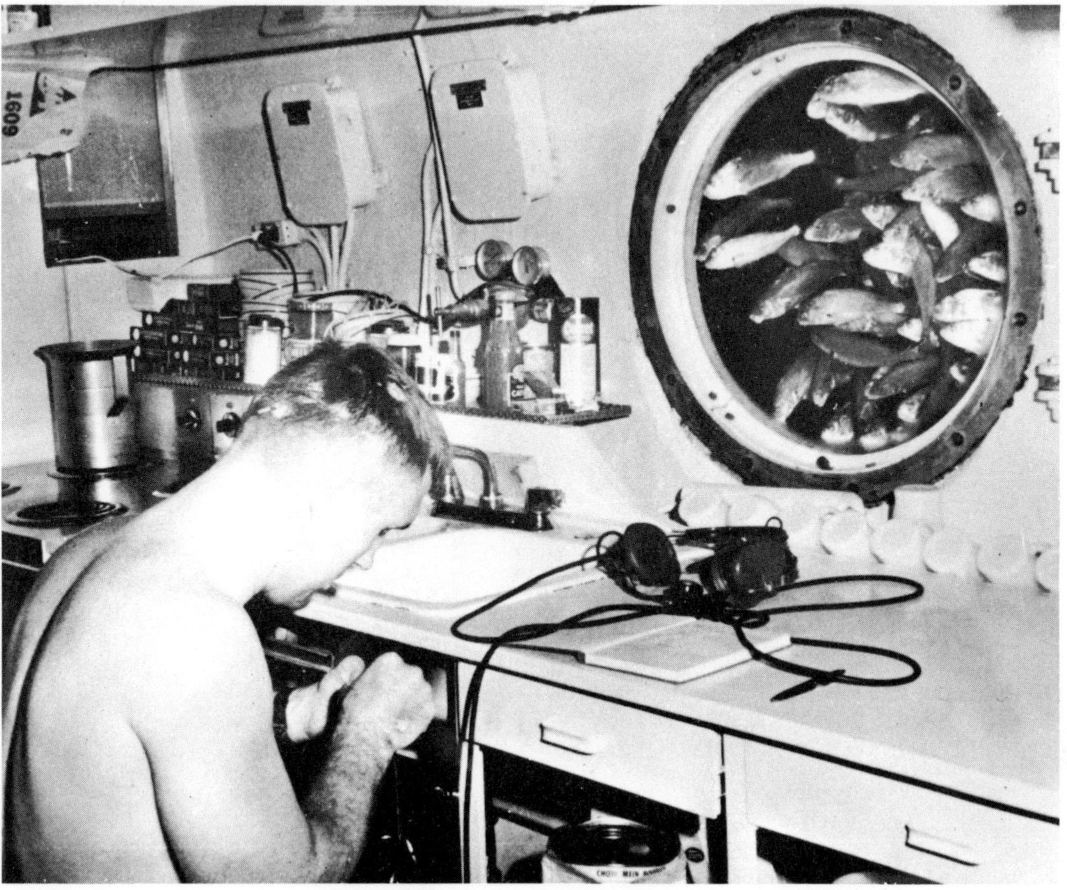

5 Breaking the Spell

Modern medical science may have its roots in the primitive magic of the past, but it also has a new counter-magic of its own—the knowledge and discoveries that, all over the world, are breaking the age-old spell of sickness and disease.

In 323 B.C. Alexander the Great died, at the age of 33, by the waters of Babylon. In the third century A.D. two great empires, the Roman Empire in the West and the Han Empire in China, were tottering. The death of the emperor and, to a large extent, the fate of the empires have been ascribed to malaria.

This disease has dominated the world throughout the centuries, changing the course of history and causing vast tracts of land to be abandoned. Today it is possible to sweep it from the face of the earth.

"Malaria" means "bad air," and two thousand four hundred years ago Empedocles tried to protect Selinus, in his native land of Sicily, by draining the nearby swamps from which the mists and "bad air" came. We now know that the air had nothing to do with the disease, but Empedocles was successful nevertheless. By draining the swamps he robbed the disease-carrying mosquitoes of their breeding-grounds.

The real cause of malaria was discovered at the end of the last century, when Alphonse Laveran identified the malarial parasite☞ in human blood and Sir Ronald Ross showed how the anopheles mosquito put it there. Quite soon the draining of swamps and the spraying of breeding places with oil helped to clear the disease from tropical countries. Doctors were able to treat patients with quinine—an Inca drug introduced into Europe by a Jesuit priest in the 17th century. During World War II, when little quinine was available, synthetic drugs, which proved superior, were used.

The great advance came after the war, however, when DDT and other effective insecticides first became generally available. Sardinia and Cyprus were quickly cleared of the disease, and campaigns for its

Mask worn by Ceylonese "devil dancers" to cure people of catarrh.

control elsewhere were launched by governments and international organizations. It was found necessary only to spray the walls on which blood-sucking mosquitoes rested. In this way a large number of adult insects, which suck malarial blood from the sick and carry it to the healthy, were killed off. There were few left to breed and produce another generation.

But some mosquitoes—a small proportion—have a natural resistance to insecticides. They escape and, while the rest are being killed off, they multiply and, in a few years, produce a mosquito population immune to poisons. Faced with this possibility, governments decided, in 1955, on a worldwide simultaneous campaign to get rid of malaria so that these resistant insects will have no parasites to transmit. Already, many areas that were once almost uninhabitable because of malaria are being cultivated.

Man has successfully come to grips with many carriers of infectious disease and is steadily extending his understanding of those diseases that originate in his own body.

With the resources of medical knowledge, the span of life has been increased. The great majority of children now survive the ailments of infancy and childhood that used to claim so many victims. Modern prevention, treatment, and drugs hold at bay the killer diseases that, only a few years ago, seemed as inexorable as Fate. Although in under-developed countries the average expectation of life of a baby at birth is still less than thirty years, the average in the advanced countries is seventy years—the biblical life-span of three score years and ten.

A group of Indian children studying a model of the malaria-carrying mosquito.

Fighting sickness, however, is one thing. Achieving sound health is something different. As the Charter of the World Health Organization says: "Health is a state of complete physical, mental and social well-being and not merely the absence of disease or infirmity. The enjoyment of the highest attainable standard of health is one of the fundamental rights of every human being."

The life history of the ordinary person has completely changed since Shakespeare described the Seven Ages of Man. People of *all* ages can now think not merely of survival or existence, but can enjoy a well-being that gives a richness to living.

This is what is meant by "Positive Health"—something we can take for granted as a regular, normal state and not as an occasional respite from ailments. This is something that derives neither from magic nor from medicine. Medicine, with other branches of science, has done much to produce conditions in which health is possible, but no doctor can prescribe health. Health must always rest largely with the individual—the Whole Man, in his own private world of a sound mind and a fit body.

A WHO malaria team makes its way into the Indian jungle on an elephant's back.

Greek coin records Empedocles' fight against malaria in the fifth century B.C.

Glossary

In this Glossary, as in the rest of the book, the symbol☞ means that the term it follows has its own alphabetical entry in the Glossary, to which you may refer for a fuller definition or for more information.

ABSCESS A cavity in tissue, caused by an infection☞, that fills with pus☞. More serious abscesses may need to be surgically opened.

ADDICTION A powerful habit—such as drug-taking—which the addict finds difficult or impossible to break, and which often cannot be broken without physical or emotional distress.

ADRENALIN A hormone☞ secreted by the suprarenal gland☞, which prepares the body to meet an emergency. It speeds the flow of blood to the muscles, increases the production of glucose for energy, and so on.

ALLERGY A violent physical reaction—such as a rash, skin blisters, or an attack of asthma—suffered by some people when in contact with substances that normally have no such effect on most others.

ANALGESIA Reduced sensibility to pain. Drugs that deaden pain are called analgesics.

ANEMIA A disease that reduces the number of erythrocytes☞ (red cells) in the blood. It is usually caused by loss of blood or by inadequate diet. In a more serious form, called "pernicious" anemia, the disease is due to the failure of the bone marrow to manufacture red blood cells—which is usually due to a dietary deficiency.

ANESTHESIA Properly meaning insensibility or loss of feeling, the term has come to mean a deliberately induced insensibility—up to and including complete unconsciousness—for the purpose of performing surgery.

ANGINA PECTORIS One of the two most common forms (with coronary thrombosis☞) of "heart attack." Symptoms include severe pain and a sensation of compression in the region of the left shoulder and arm. The attack may be brought on by overexertion, anxiety, or sudden shock, and in many cases will disappear with proper medical care.

ANTIBIOTIC Literally "opposed to life." A substance, derived from living materials such as molds or fungi, used to counteract infection.

Early chloroform inhaler, about 1858.

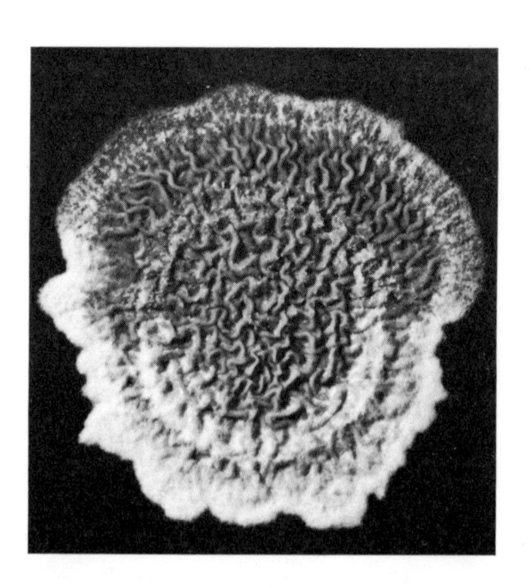

Mold yielding Cephalosporins, a newly researched group of antibiotics.

Antiseptics are applied to wounds, to kill the germs that cause infection.

ANTIBODIES Substances produced in the blood; they neutralize the action of disease-producing bacteria☞ or chemical agents. The immunity☞ they confer is one of the body's natural defenses against disease.

ANTICOAGULANT A drug that reduces the ability of the blood to coagulate or clot: useful in treating such conditions as coronary thrombosis, caused by a blood clot blocking the flow of blood to the heart.

ANTISEPTIC Properly, any substance that inhibits the process of putrefaction. But the word's common usage includes the meaning of "disinfectant": a substance that destroys the germs that cause infection.

ARTERIES The branching blood vessels that carry the blood from the heart throughout the body.

ARTHRITIS A painful inflammation of a joint or joints. "Rheumatoid" arthritis (the cause of which remains unknown) affects the hands and feet especially. "Osteoarthritis" afflicts mostly old people.

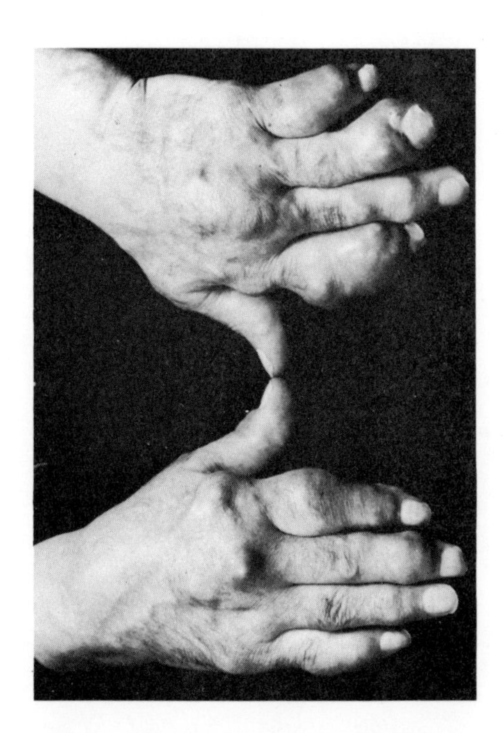

Hands affected by rheumatoid arthritis —primarily a disease of old age.

AUTONOMIC NERVOUS SYSTEM That part of the nervous system operating automatic bodily functions—the heartbeat, digestion, processes of the glands, and so on. This system has two subdivisions: the "sympathetic," which prepares the body for energetic or emergency action, and the "parasympathetic," which prepares the body for rest. See CENTRAL NERVOUS SYSTEM.

BACTERIA A general term for organisms visible only through microscopes. Some are disease-producing, some are harmless, some are beneficial. Of harmful bacteria, the more commonly known forms are bacilli, cocci, spirilla, spirochetes, staphylococci, and streptococci.

BARBITURATES Sedative or sleep-inducing drugs, obtainable by doctor's prescription, and dangerous in an overdose.

BLOOD GROUPS Classification of human blood into four groups, under the letters A, B, AB, and O. (All human beings belong to one or another of these groups, or types. The type O is the most common.) For successful blood transfusion the blood to be given must belong to the same type as the recipient's own blood, otherwise it would be rejected as though it were "foreign matter."

BLOOD PRESSURE Pressure exerted by the blood on the walls of the arteries☞ as it is pumped into them by the heart.

CANCER A dangerous and widespread disease characterized by the growth of a malignant tumor☞. It occurs in two principal forms: *carcinoma*—cancer of some surface of the body (including the surfaces and linings of internal organs); and *sarcoma*—cancer occurring within actual tissue—of muscle, bone, etc. (Carcinoma is by far the more common.) If detected early enough, cancer can generally be cured—by radiotherapy☞ or surgery.

CENTRAL NERVOUS SYSTEM Also called the *cerebrospinal* system. It is composed of the brain, the spinal cord, and a network of nerves branching throughout the body. This system, which is mostly under conscious control, includes the sensory nerves that carry sense impressions to the brain, and the motor nerves through which the brain directs body movements. But the various automatic reflexes☞ are also produced through the cerebrospinal system.

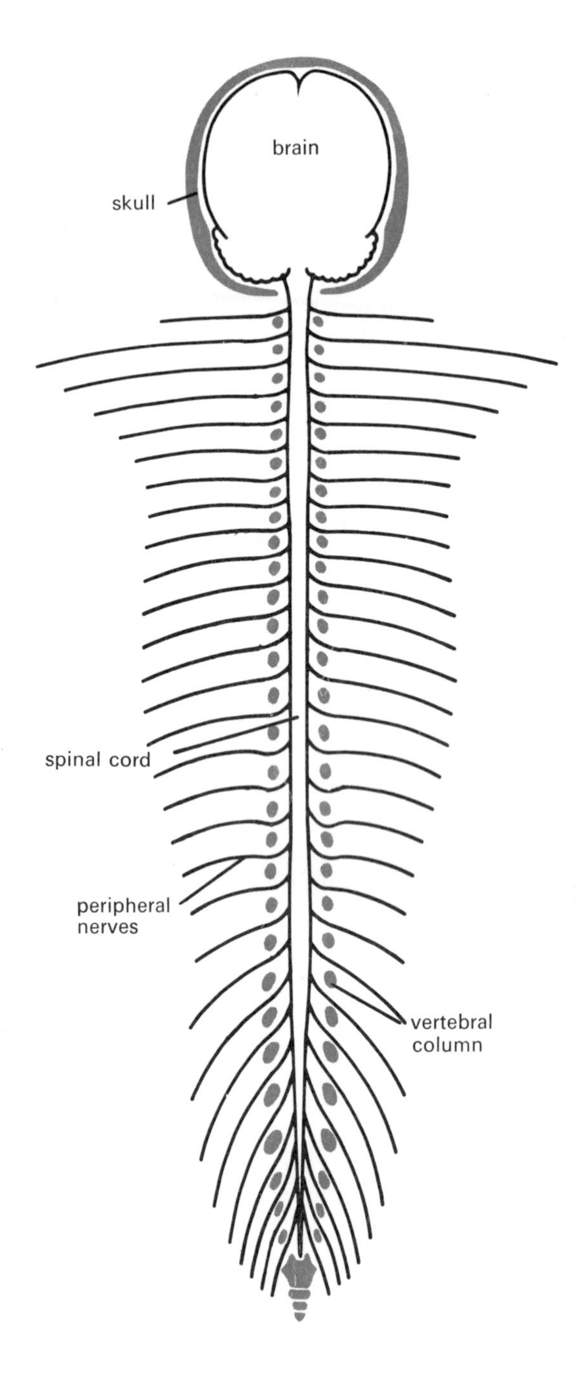

Diagram of the central nervous system.

CHROMOSOMES Microscopic bodies existing in the nucleus of every human cell. They carry the genes☞ that determine the nature of the individual body's development. Each cell contains 48 chromosomes, with the exception of the male sperm cell and the female ovum. These have 24 each: when they unite, to begin the growth of a new human being, they form a cell with 48 chromosomes. As the cells divide over and over during the growth process, the chromosomes divide as well to maintain the required number in every cell.

COMA Unconsciousness, so deep that even the reflexes☞ no longer operate. A coma can be caused, for example, by an overdose of some narcotic drug, a severe head injury, a brain hemorrhage☞, or a high fever.

Medieval leper carrying a rattle, to warn others of the risk of contagion.

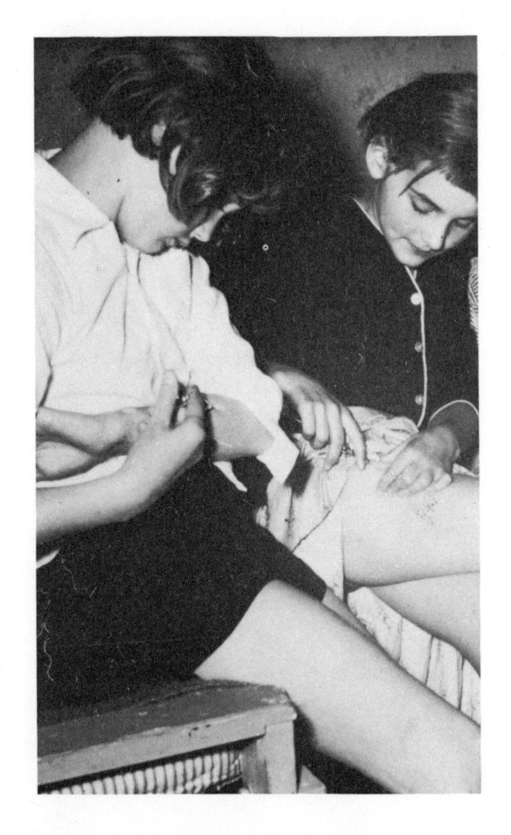

Diabetic children who have learned how to give themselves insulin.

CONGENITAL Referring to illnesses or defects that are present in a baby at birth. Such disorders may be inherited from the parents, but not necessarily: many result from the mother's being in a condition of ill health during pregnancy.

CONTAGION The spreading of disease by means of physical contact with germ-carrying persons, or substances.

CORONARY THROMBOSIS A failure of the blood supply to the heart, causing symptoms very like those of angina pectoris☞: pain in the region of the heart, spreading to the left shoulder and arm, a sense of compression, and shock☞. It is said to be the most common cause of instantaneous death. The failure itself is due to a clotting of the blood in the *coronary* arteries☞ that carry blood to the muscles of the heart.

CORPUSCLE A minute particle, or cell, usually used in terms of blood cells.

CORTISONE A hormone☞ secreted by the suprarenal glands☞, found to be useful in the treatment of arthritis☞.

DEFICIENCY DISEASES Diseases caused by inadequate diet, especially by insufficient vitamins☞ in the diet—scurvy and rickets, for example.

DIABETES A disease caused by a disorder of the pancreas☞—the gland that secretes the hormone insulin☞, which controls the body's utilization of sugar. In diabetes the unused sugar is excreted in the urine. Sufferers may exhibit symptoms ranging from general weakness to deep coma☞ and even gangrene. Mild cases can be treated by a special diet; serious cases must receive regular injections of insulin under medical supervision.

DYSENTERY A severe form of diarrhea, usually including bleeding from the bowels. The dysentery caused by bacteria☞ is generally prevalent where unsanitary conditions exist; the sulfonamide☞ drugs are used in its treatment. Another form of dysentery, caused by amoebas (single-celled, microscopic animal life) is mainly a tropical disease.

DYSTROPHY A disease caused by defective nutrition. One common form is muscular dystrophy, an incurable wasting disease (affecting mainly children) in which the muscles of the lower body and legs grow progressively weaker.

ELECTROCARDIOGRAPH An instrument that records any changes in electrical potential that take place in the heart as it beats. The record itself is called an electrocardiogram, and will show—for purposes of diagnosis—any abnormality in the heart's action.

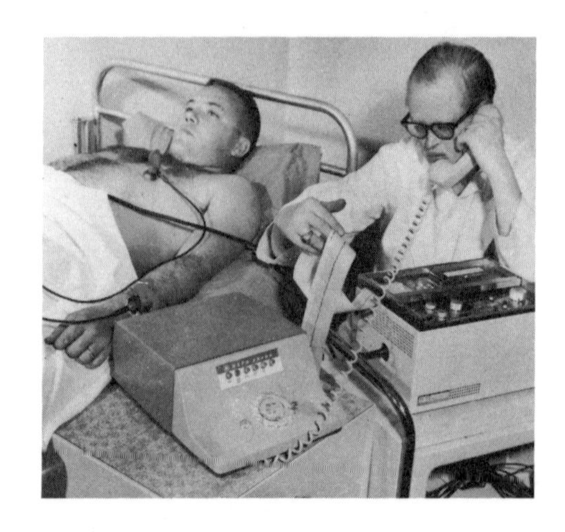

An electrocardiogram is electronically transmitted to a distant specialist; the doctor awaits his diagnosis.

ENDOCRINE GLANDS The ductless glands—organs that secrete substances essential for physical development and growth, for the control of bodily functions, for sexual and emotional development, and more. These glands discharge their secretions directly into the blood, rather than through ducts.

ERYTHROCYTES The red cells of the blood. Their main function is to carry oxygen from the lungs to the parts of the body, and to carry waste products such as carbon dioxide back to the lungs for exhalation.

ETIOLOGY The study of the causes of disease.

EUTHANASIA The popular term is "mercy killing": putting to death people who are suffering from a painful and incurable disease. The subject remains extremely controversial. Believers in euthanasia feel that it is inhuman to let people die an agonized death when the inevitable end could be brought on painlessly.

FORENSIC MEDICINE Medicine in association with courts of law. The term includes the use of medical knowledge by the police.

FRINGE MEDICINE Medical beliefs and practices that are generally not considered to be legitimately part of orthodox, scientific medicine. In many cases it is practiced by people who lack accepted medical qualifications.

Patent medicine poster, 19th century.

GAMMA GLOBULIN The protein part of the blood, from which the antibodies☞ are produced to form immunity☞ to disease.

In England, a mobile catering service, subsidized by local authorities, provides meals for the aged and disabled.

GENES Submicroscopic organisms, carried by the chromosomes☞, that govern the growth and development of the body in terms of inherited characteristics.

GERIATRICS The study of the problems and diseases of old age.

GRAFTING The removal of a piece of tissue from a plant, animal, or human, and its "transplanting" elsewhere in the same organism, or in another. Skin grafts, for instance, are made to repair damage caused by burns and other accidents. Usually such grafts involve the removal of healthy skin from another part of the injured person's body. Bone grafting, too, is a familiar operation. The introduction of living tissue from one person's body into another's can set off the same reaction as the introduction of disease bacteria: the recipient's body creates antibodies☞ to destroy the intruder. For this reason, grafting whole organs (for instance, kidneys) from one person to another has not yet been wholly successful. But medical science seems to be on the threshold of a breakthrough in this field.

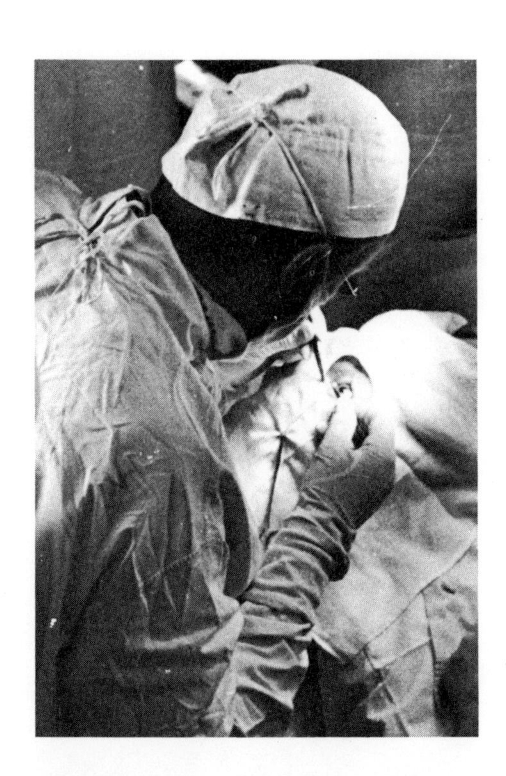

Cutting a corneal section for grafting.

HEMOGLOBIN A protein material in the blood that gives the red cells their color, and is the actual carrier of oxygen from the lungs to the body's tissues. See ERYTHROCYTES.

HEMORRHAGE Any flow of blood. If from a cut or damaged artery☞, the flow comes in spurts (as the heart beats) and is bright red. From an injured vein☞, the flow is steady and dark.

HORMONES Substances, secreted by the endocrine glands☞, that influence a great many bodily processes.

HYPERTENSION Excessive "tension," or pressure of bodily fluid, most usually synonymous with high blood pressure☞. Modern medicine suspects a connection between high blood pressure and action of the endocrine glands☞. But the sufferer's state of mind (anxiety, frustration, etc.) also forces up blood pressure, and many doctors will treat the condition as they would treat any psychosomatic illness☞.

HYPNOSIS The method of artificially inducing a "trance"—a sleep-like semiconscious state that leaves the hypnotized person more open to suggestion. Though it is often demeaned as stage entertainment, the practice has definite wide-ranging medical value. It offers an easy form of anesthesia☞ (used in dentistry and childbirth); it is also valuable in psychiatry as a means of locating the cause of psychosomatic illness☞.

HYPOCHONDRIA The belief that one is suffering from a physical disease—or diseases—when no medical evidence exists of the disease's presence.

HYPODERMIC Literally "under the skin," referring most commonly to injections, but also to the syringe used to administer injections.

HYSTERIA Colloquially the term means any outbreak of excessive emotionalism. But in medical practice hysteria is a psychological disorder that has as a primary symptom great emotional excitability. Other symptoms include "dissociation" (where one part of the mind seems to be cut off from the rest), a high susceptibility to suggestion, and "repression" of certain emotions or memories.

IMMUNITY The ability to resist disease. Many people seem to have natural immunity against certain diseases. Others must acquire immunity either by contracting the disease, recovering from it, and retaining the antibodies☞ that were produced to fight it; or by receiving a vaccination or inoculation☞.

INCUBATION Generally, the term refers to the process of maintaining delicate organisms (eggs, prematurely-born babies, etc.) under conditions that will protect and nurture them. In terms of disease, the "incubation period" means the time that elapses between a person's being infected and the appearance of the first symptoms.

INFECTION The spreading of disease-carrying microorganisms by direct or indirect means.

INFLUENZA A general name for a wide variety of diseases, from the minor ailment that causes two or three days' discomfort to the killer disease

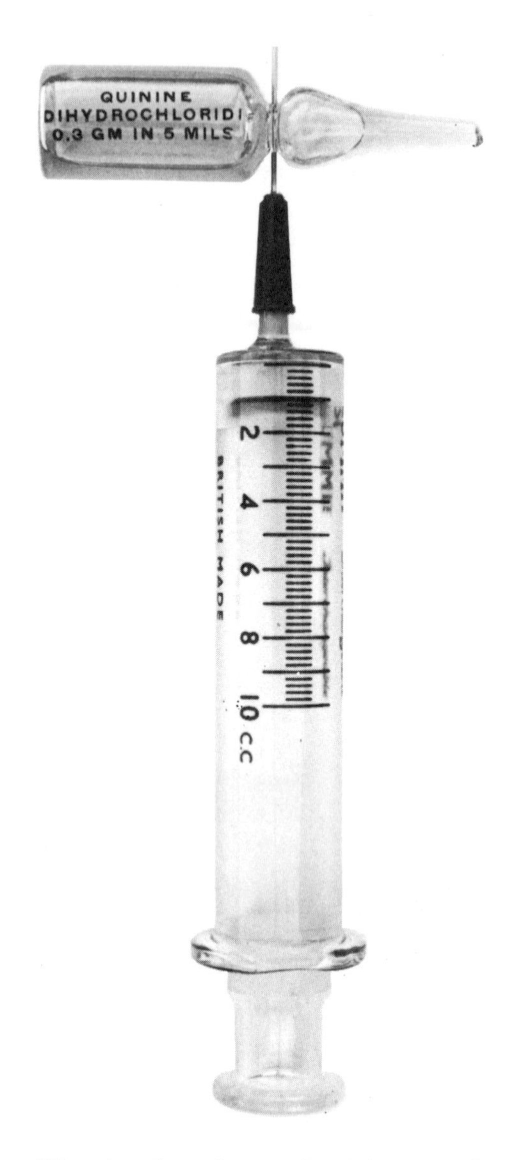

Hypodermic syringe and quinine ampul.

Sneezing and coughing are among the most common causes of infection.

Nursing through the Ages *"Nursing" originally meant looking after children. Nuns cared for the sick and the dying; neither they, nor the early 19th century "watcher," were trained.*

In 1860, Florence Nightingale founded her training school for nurses at St. Thomas's Hospital, London; its influence changed nursing into an organized and respected profession. Post-Nightingale nurses, like this hospital matron of 1911 (right), were well-trained, efficient, and neat.

from which millions died in the world wide epidemic of 1918–19. Viruses☞ are the cause of the disease—but many different forms of virus.

James Gillray's 18th-century cartoon satirizing early fears about the effects of inoculation with cowpox vaccine.

INOCULATION The injection of weakened or dead infectious matter, in order to stimulate the body's defenses against the disease and thus create immunity☞.

INSULIN The hormone secreted in the pancreas☞. It enables those tissues that require sugar to absorb it from the blood. See DIABETES.

INTRAVENOUS Literally, within a vein. Blood transfusions are made intravenously.

LEUCOCYTES The white blood cells. Normal blood contains about 5000 leucocytes per cubic millimeter. They are produced mainly in the bone marrow, the spleen, and the lymph glands☞. Different types of leucocytes exist: of these the phagocytes and lymphocytes are perhaps the most numerous. Their function is to help defend the body against invading bacteria. Once the antibodies have rendered the bacteria harmless, the leucocytes ingest them and absorb any dead tissue cells left from the invasion.

A 19th-century photograph showing two boys of the same age: a schoolboy fed on a balanced diet, and a mine-worker suffering from malnutrition.

LEUKEMIA A disease of the blood-forming organs (also of the bone marrow), in which the number of leucocytes☞ in the blood is greatly increased, and the erythrocytes☞ decreased. An acute form of the disease is believed to result from exposure to radioactivity; it usually affects children, and so far remains incurable. Chronic leukemia affects older adults, and resembles a cancerous condition. But the chronic form is not so quickly fatal as the acute, and can be susceptible to radiotherapy☞ and some drugs.

LYMPH GLANDS They are found throughout the body, especially at "junctions": for example, at the knee and elbow. They produce lymph and lymphocytes; they function in the digestive process that carries nourishment to the cells; and they form a bastion against infection.

MALNUTRITION A state of general weakness and susceptibility to disease, that is the result of inadequate diet.

French reformer Philippe Pinel (1745-1826) ordering an assistant to unchain insane patients in a Paris hospital.

MANIC DEPRESSION A psychosis☞ in which the sufferer's state alternates between irrational elation and deep, morbid depression.

MENTAL ILLNESS Abnormality of the mind, making its appearance in the person's behavior, social relationships, etc. Where mental defects are mostly the concern of medical doctors, mental illnesses mostly enter into the less concrete realm of psychology☞. (But a few mental illnesses have their roots in physical disease—for instance, alcoholic poisoning—and will be treated by medical means.) Mental disorders range from mild neuroses☞, through the well-known psychoses☞ such as manic depression☞ or schizophrenia☞, to the psychopathic disorders of the incurably insane.

METABOLISM A general term for the body's "life" processes: the utilization of food, air, and so on in the continual construction and repair of blood, tissue, bone, etc. The "metabolic rate" is the speed at which these processes run.

Lawyer's evidence: a hoard of narcotics discovered in the hollowed-out heel of a would-be smuggler's shoe.

NARCOTICS In medical terms, a narcotic is simply any drug capable of inducing unconsciousness (i.e., "narcosis"). But in common usage the term is often applied to such dangerous drugs of addiction as cocaine, or opium and its derivatives morphine and heroin; also to other addictive or semi-addictive drugs that are not sleep-inducing, such as marijuana.

NEUROSIS A form of mental disorder. It might be an "anxiety state"—a general nervousness or apprehension without apparent reason, sometimes focused into one of the "phobias" (*claustrophobia*—fear of enclosures; *agoraphobia*—fear of open spaces; etc.). Or a neurosis might occur as a personality disorder, such as hysteria☞. Or it might produce "obsessions"—compulsive, habitual, but apparently irrational patterns of thought or action. Generally a neurosis arises out of some form of maladjustment (with its roots in the sufferer's early life) preventing normal conduct or relationships with people.

PANCREAS The large gland situated behind the stomach. It produces digestive fluids, and discharges them through a duct. Yet it also secretes the hormone insulin☞, which it discharges (like the endocrine glands☞) directly into the blood, without a duct. See DIABETES.

PARASITES Animal life that infests and lives off the human body. External parasites include lice, fleas, and bedbugs. Internal parasites mainly take the form of worms, such as the tapeworm, hookworm, or ringworm. In most cases these parasites are picked up by means of infested food inadequately prepared—for example, pork, fish, or fowl eaten raw or half-cooked. Often the worms live entirely in the human intestines; but more dangerous ones (found mainly in underdeveloped, tropical countries) might take up residence in other organs, or in the limbs, causing serious disorders.

PARATHYROID GLANDS Four small glands, lying behind the thyroid, that govern the body's use of calcium and phosphorus.

PATHOLOGY The study of disease, especially of the changes in the body and in tissue resulting from disease.

PENTOTHAL A barbiturate☞, commonly (and loosely) called the "truth drug." It is a widely used general anesthetic☞, especially in relatively brief operations.

PHYSIOTHERAPY The physical treatment of disease (and often of the bodily weakness left by some diseases) by means of heat treatment, massage, controlled exercise, bathing (hydrotherapy), and more.

PITUITARY GLAND An endocrine gland☞ situated at the base of the brain. Part of the gland produces two hormones☞, one controlling blood pressure and urine, the other (in women) causing contractions of the womb in childbirth. The other part of the pituitary has a central function in the body's overall development and well-being. Thus a disorder of the gland can cause dwarfism or gigantism, gross obesity or wasting, and similar disruptions of the growth processes. Also, this part of the pituitary produces hormones that stimulate and control the other endocrine glands.

Dusting an Iranian boy with insecticide to free him from external parasites.

Surgery Today *Surgeons, nurses, and technicians combine their skills to perform a wonderfully complex operation: inserting a plastic "bypass" pump to revive a patient's failing heart.*

PLASMA The fluid of the blood, in which the corpuscles☞ are contained. It is composed of serum☞ and fibrinogen.

PLASTIC SURGERY The form of surgery that reconstructs some damaged or deformed part of the body. For example, it is used widely to repair facial injuries; or to graft new skin onto a burned area; or to overcome congenital☞ deformities.

PROPRIETARY A term used for a medicine or drug when it is manufactured under a specific name by a specific firm. For example, acetylsalicylic acid is best known under the proprietary name of "aspirin"; but the same substance appears as an ingredient of similar remedies that bear different trade names.

PSYCHIATRY The study of the causes and especially the treatment of mental illness☞. It is a branch of medical science: psychiatrists are medical doctors.

PSYCHOANALYSIS A method of treating mentally disturbed or neurotic people by tracing the disturbance to its root causes. Basically psychoanalysis states that every mind has an "unconscious" as well as a conscious side; and that much of a neurotic's behavior is caused by "repressed" thoughts or memories—i.e., those he has forced into his unconscious in order to avoid facing them. (They might, for instance, be unpleasant memories from childhood, or feelings of inferiority, etc.) Nevertheless, these repressions still have an effect on his conscious mind and outward actions. Psychoanalysis seeks to bring them into the light—on the principle, to put it simply, that when they are faced, accepted, and understood they will no longer have their invidious effect. In a more elaborated form psychoanalytic theories differ widely, depending on whether they are those of Sigmund Freud (who pioneered the practice) or of his followers C. G. Jung, Alfred Adler, and others. The process of analysis can differ for the same reason: in the Freudian method it consists mainly of random rambling talk from a couch ("free association") whereas the Jungian method relies mainly on the analysis of dreams.

A roadside plasma "bank" in Germany, equipped to give emergency transfusions to accident victims.

The consulting room of Sigmund Freud (1856-1939).

Detail from a painting by a 68-year-old schizophrenic patient.

PSYCHOLOGY The study of human behavior and of the workings of the mind (mostly of the normal mind).

PSYCHOSIS Serious mental disorder; insanity. The more commonly known psychoses include manic depression☞ and schizophrenia☞.

PSYCHOSOMATIC ILLNESS A physical disorder that grows out of psychological causes. A disturbed mind, acting through and on the nervous system and the glands, produces the symptoms of an illness when no physical cause exists.

PSYCHOTHERAPY Treatment of mental illness that may include psychoanalysis, re-education, mutual discussion of problems among several people ("group therapy"), and more.

RADIOLOGY The study of radioactive substances and of X rays☞, and their use in diagnosis and treatment of disease.

RADIOTHERAPY The use of radiation in the treatment of disease, especially of cancer☞. "Gamma" rays produced by radioactive material (such as radium or radioactive cobalt) are directed onto the malignant growth. X rays☞ are also used in this form of treatment. Radiotherapy tends to be most useful in treating the slower-growing cancers, such as of the face, lip, skin, or breast.

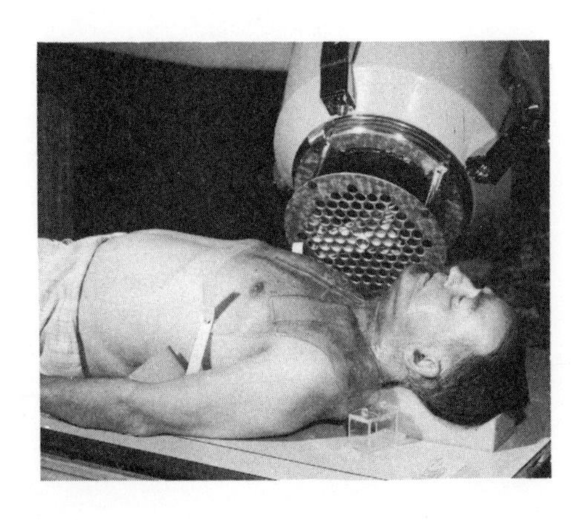

Radiotherapy: using powerful new X-ray equipment to treat a cancer.

REFLEX An automatic reaction by some part of the body to an outward stimulus: for example, the hand's jerking away from a red-hot surface. The "message" that causes the reflex does not need to penetrate to the higher, conscious-control centers of the brain. It can be sent by the lower, unconscious, "instinctive" areas of the brain. Some reflex actions, however, are not instinctive—in the sense that they need to be learned or acquired by constant repetition, until the response becomes automatic. These are "conditioned" reflexes—such as the car driver's automatic response to danger on the road.

RHEUMATISM A common term for a group of vaguely related diseases. Rheumatoid arthritis☞ causes disabling pain in the joints (especially fingers and toes). No cure has been found, but the hormone cortisone offers some relief. Rheumatic fever also causes pain in the joints—but this illness is definitely known to be a bacterial infection☞, and can be overcome by penicillin.

SCHIZOPHRENIA A psychosis☞ in which the sufferer displays wildly irrational behavior that might include serious delusions and even hallucinations. Often, too, it gives rise to a strong "dissociation" in which the mind or personality of the sufferer seems to be "split" or divided against itself.

SECRETION Material (in ordinary usage, fluid) contained in a cell or organ, to be discharged when needed.

SEPSIS A localized condition (i.e., existing in some form of wound) of being infected by pus-producing bacteria.

SERUM The fluid part of the blood without the corpuscles and also without the fibrinogen that causes clotting. The term is also used for the material used in inoculation☞ against certain diseases, such as diphtheria or tetanus. In this form of immunization a person is injected not with weak or dead microbes of the disease itself, but with serum taken from the blood of an animal that has previously been immunized against the disease.

SHOCK In its mild form, the condition is simply one of great distress and agitation caused by some disturbing occurrence. A more serious form of shock results from bodily injury—for example, an accident or surgery.

STAPHYLOCOCCI A form of bacteria shaped much like a bunch of grapes. They are prominent among the microbes that cause pus formation—as in boils, eczema, and other skin ailments.

STERILIZATION The destruction of all micro-organisms on a particular object or within a particular area. Surgical instruments, for instance, are sterilized by means of steam. The term also refers to the process of rendering a person unable to have children.

Upper, two wild rabbits: the left one is normal, the other has been subjected to a form of shock (a barking dog). Lower, their respective thyroids.

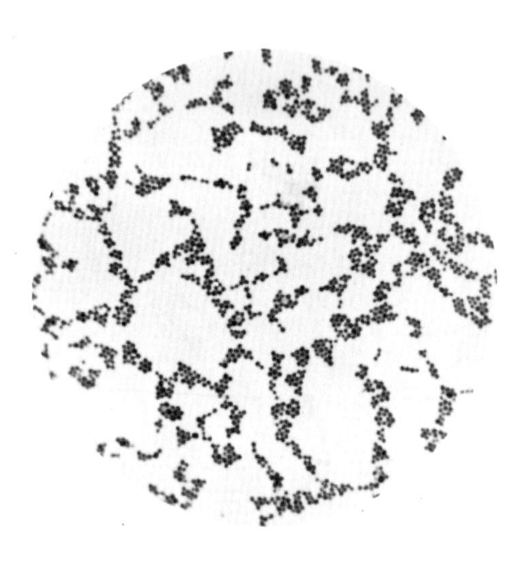

Staphylococci (magnified 900 times).

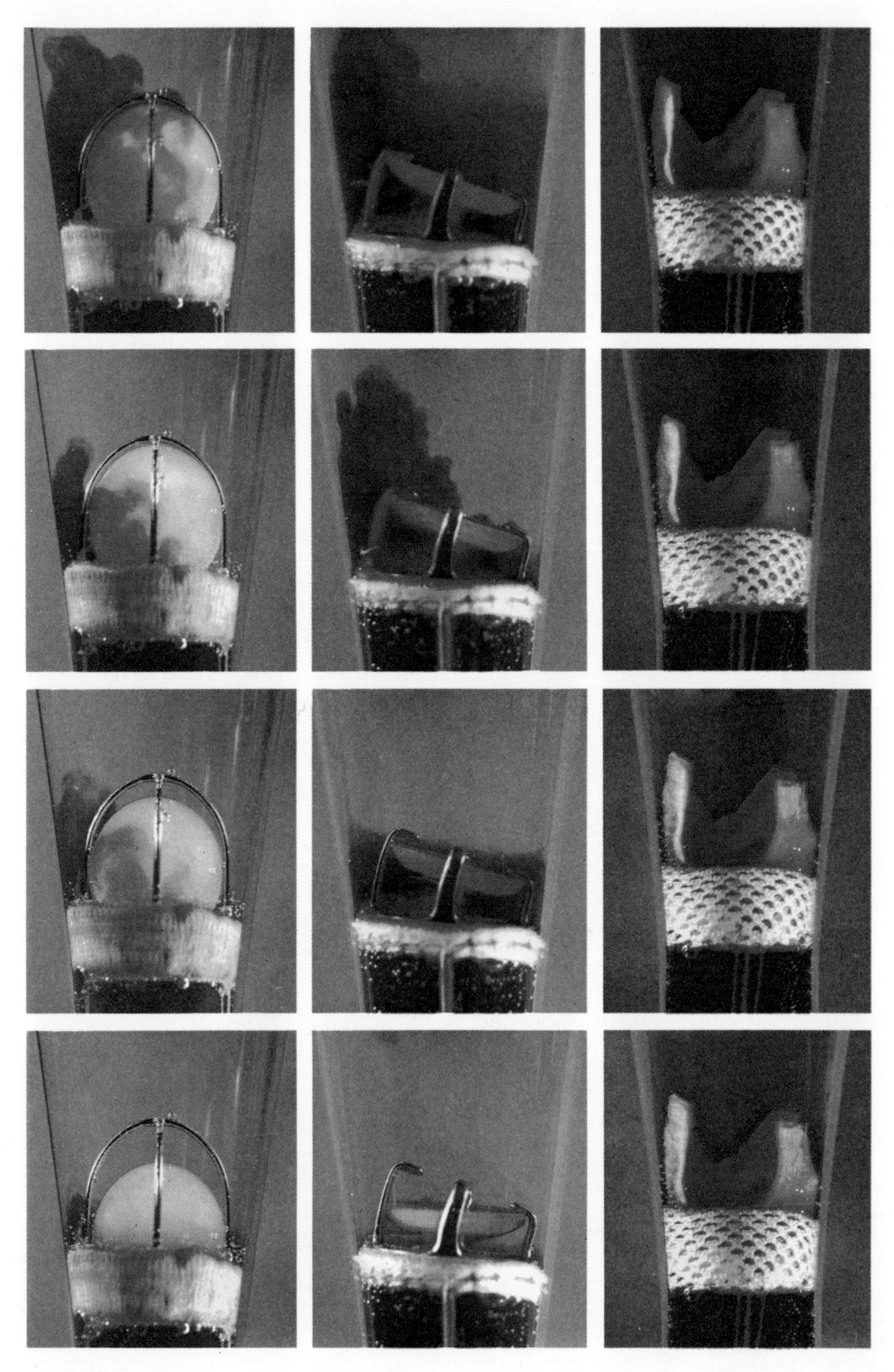

Spare Parts *Pictures compare the work of two artificial heart valves (left and center) with that of a grafted human heart valve (right). The degree to which the red fluid evenly colors the space above each valve shows how smoothly that valve is able to deliver blood.*

STREPTOCOCCI A form of bacteria shaped roughly like a chain. They can cause (among other things) serious forms of blood poisoning.

SULFONAMIDES Also called the "sulfa drugs," these substances are used in the treatment of bacterial infection☞. They do not kill bacteria, but prevent them from reproducing.

TOXIN A poison formed by animal or vegetable means. In medicine the term is usually applied to poisons formed by bacterial action.

TRANQUILIZERS A general term applied to a group of drugs, recently developed, that have a relaxing, calming effect without actually producing sleep.

TRANSFUSION Medically, the term is used mostly with reference to blood transfusions; these can be made directly from one person to another, but today it is more common to transfuse blood that has been stored in a "blood bank."

TUBERCULOSIS An infectious disease caused by bacteria that can attack the body in many areas—most commonly in the lungs, bones, or intestines. The bacteria break down tissue to form pus; often the wound will heal, but in some cases the bacteria (if not stopped by treatment) will eat their way through surrounding tissue and, especially when in the lungs, will shortly lead to death. The bacteria are spread by infected humans (through coughing or direct contact), infected animal products, and so on. Widespread preventative measures have come into operation in recent years—including mass X rays and vaccination.

TUMOR Any growth or swelling. Some tumors are "benign"—i.e., not dangerous in themselves and not likely to spread. Others are "malignant"—i.e., cancerous.

ULCER Any open sore—though the term is most often applied to internal sores. A *gastric* or stomach ulcer occurs when the digestive juices act on the stomach wall—and in fact digest part of the wall. Treatment involves a careful diet of bland foods—and also, perhaps, a prescription

A typical tranquilizer (magnified), containing a series of timed doses.

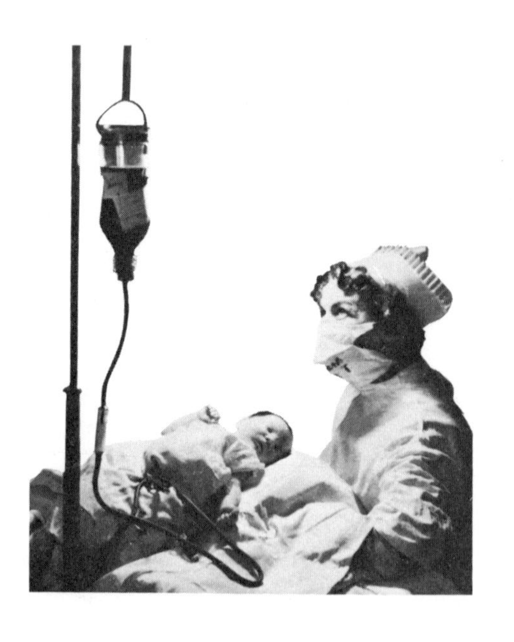

A complete change of blood at birth may save the life of a "Rhesus" baby.

Italian bronze showing Edward Jenner (1749-1823) vaccinating a child.

As part of Israel's health service, a mobile X-ray unit visits the nomads.

of sedatives or tranquilizers, due to the close connection between stomach ulcers and mental stress or anxiety. Even more common than the gastric ulcer is the *duodenal* ulcer—where the digestive juices attack the walls of the duodenum, the first 10 inches of the small intestine. If the digestive juices eat entirely through the wall of the stomach or the duodenum, the ulcer is said to be "perforated."

VACCINATION The injection of weakened or dead infectious matter into a healthy body, to provide immunity☞ against the particular disease. The term is used most frequently in terms of smallpox; in this case the vaccine is scratched into the skin, not injected deep into the tissue. But the term can of course be applied to the giving of any vaccine.

VEINS The branching blood vessels that carry the blood from the various parts of the body back to the heart.

VIRUSES Disease-carrying microorganisms, smaller than bacteria. (Viruses cannot be seen by ordinary microscopes, but need the extra power of an electron microscope.) Virus diseases include smallpox, poliomyelitis, various children's diseases, and (it seems) the common cold.

VITAMINS Chemical substances in food that are essential, in small quantities, for growth, development and well-being. Vitamins are distinguished by letters, sometimes by letters and numerals.

X RAYS Electromagnetic waves, much shorter than light waves, and so able to pass through certain materials that light cannot penetrate, X rays are widely used in diagnosis, since with them the interior of the body can be "photographed." The rays pass through flesh more easily than through bone, so the bones are clearly outlined on the film exposed to the rays. X rays are also used for treating skin growths—not only skin cancers, but such benign growths as warts. And the X rays emitted by radioactive materials can be used to treat deeper cancers—since malignant cells are affected by radioactivity sooner than healthy cells.

Index

Page numbers in *italics* refer to illustration captions.

Picture Credits

Endpapers: British Museum/Photos John Freeman
8 (R) The Department of History of Medicine, University of Kansas Medical Center, Kansas City

11 Royal College of Surgeons of England/Photo Michael Holford
12 (L) The Royal Collection, Windsor Castle: copyright reserved
15 (TR) Photo D. Ellis
(B) Photo Donald Longmore
17 Mansell Collection
18 Photo D. Ellis
21 From Hilaire Cuny, *Pavlov*, Collection Savants du Monde Entier, Editions Seghers, Paris
22 (T) From *The Human Machine: Mechanisms*, Thomas Nelson & Sons Ltd., Publishers, London; Salvat Editores, S.A., Barcelona; Editions Kister, Geneva, 1961
25 Mansell Collection
26 Photos Dennis Weston, Leeds
27 United Kingdom Atomic Energy Authority
31 Ny Carlsberg Glyptotek, Copenhagen
36 Osterreichische Nationalbibliothek, Wien/Photo Lichtbildwerkstatte
37 (L) Mansell/Alinari
(R) The Swedish Embassy, London
38 National Gallery, London
43 (TR) London Express
(B) Photo Donald Longmore
44-45 (R) Photos courtesy Glaxo Laboratories Ltd.
50 United Kingdom Atomic Energy Authority
51 Photo D. Ellis
52 Mansell Collection
55 (T) Photo Prof. Dr. R. Luchsinger/Folia Phoniatrica
(CR) Courtesy The Royal National Institute for the Blind
(B) Photo by permission of the Ministry of Health
57 Artwork David Litchfield
58 Photos courtesy Smith Kline & French Laboratories Ltd.
59 British Crown Copyright
62 (T) WHO/Photo Paul Almasy
(B) WHO/Photo Jean Mohr
66 Photo courtesy British Travel Association
67 (R) Atelje Sundahl AB, Stockholm
69 (T) Photo National Aeronautics and Space Administration, Washington
(B) USIS, London
73 WHO/Photo P. N. Sharna
76 (B) Photo courtesy Glaxo Laboratories Ltd.
77 (T) WHO/Photo Paul Almasy
(B) Photo courtesy The Arthritis & Rheumatism Council
80 (T) United States Information Service
(B) The New York Historical Society
81 (T) Photo Ben May, Canterbury
(B) Odhams Press
82 (B) Photo courtesy Dr. M. W. Jennison, Syracuse University
85 (T) Photo Rapho, Paris
(B) Photo courtesy Minneapolis (Minnesota) Star
86 WHO/Photo Marc Riboud
87 *Life* © Time Inc.
88 (T) Photo Keystone
(B) Photo *Du*, Conzett & Huber, Zürich
89 (B) United States Information Service
90 (T) From Hans Selye, *Second Annual Report on Stress*, Acta Inc., Montreal
(B) Courtesy Ken Fletcher
91 Courtesy Edwards Laboratories Inc., Santa Ana, California
92 (B) P.A.-Reuter photo

Aldus Archives: 8, 9, 13, 22(B), 33(R), 39, 60, 76(T), 79(T), 83(BR)
British Museum/Photos John Freeman: 6, 10, 30, 70, 74
WHO Photo: 48, 53, 63, 79(B), 93(B)
Wellcome Historical Medical Museum: 15(TL), 16, 19(L), 28, 33(L), 35, 40, 43(TL), 46, 47, 83(BL), 84(T), 93(T)
British Museum Photographs are reproduced by courtesy of the Trustees